CRUMPY'S
CAMPFIRE
COMPANION

No reference intended to anyone in this book.

To Mum + Dad, happy Aniversary 1996
Lots of love; Graham + Corinne
xxxx   xxxx

CRUMPY'S
CAMPFIRE
COMPANION

THE THIRD OF A TRILOGY

BARRY CRUMP

Hodder Moa Beckett

ISBN 1-86958-288-8

Published in 1996 by Hodder Moa Beckett Publishers Limited
4 Whetu Place, Mairangi Bay, Auckland, New Zealand
PO Box 100 749, North Shore Mail Centre, Auckland 1330

Printed by McPhersons Print, Australia

Author's note:

Esteemed Reader,

A brief note about this book.

A while back I wrote an autobiography called *The Life and Times of a Good Keen Man*. One memory evokes another and I ended up with a lot of material I couldn't fit in the book, things that have happened, things that have partly happened, and things that might have happened. The result of this is that some of these yarns are true, some are partly true, some aren't true at all, and some I'm not too sure about myself.

I present them for your entertainment. I hope you enjoy them and if I've captured some of the atmosphere of the times and they raise a chuckle in you I'll be well pleased.

Happy reading,

Aroha,

Crumpy

Books by Barry Crump

A Good Keen Man (1960)*

Hang on a Minute Mate (1961)*

One of Us (1962)*

There and Back (1963)

Gulf (1964) – now titled Crocodile Country*

Scrapwagon (1965)

The Odd Spot of Bother (1967)

No Reference Intended (1968)

A Good Keen Girl (1970)

Bastards I Have Met (1970)*

Fred (1972)

Shorty (1980)

Puha Road (1982)

The Adventures of Sam Cash (1985)

Wild Pork and Watercress (1986)*

Barry Crump's Bedtime Yarns (1988)

Bullock Creek (1989)*

The Life and Times of a Good Keen Man (1992)

Gold and Greenstone (1993)*

Arty and the Fox (1994)*

Forty Yarns and a Song (1995)*

Mrs Windyflax and the Pungapeople (1995)*

* currently (1996) in print

Dedication

For Maggie, who comes in handy

CONTENTS

1

THE DUGGAN BROTHERS

U s Crump kids were all still in our pre-teen years
when one of our neighbours, old Charlie Duggan,
dried his cows off for the winter and then turned up
his toes. "Returned to his maker," our mother described it, but
our old man used to say that old Charlie just got waterlogged
and sank.

Charlie had never married and we were curious to see what
was going to happen to his farm, which was appropriately
enough called Mudflat Farm. It wasn't really a farm as such, it
was a stretch of coastal swampland with a few drier patches of
ground up towards the road. It was three hundred yards from the
road to the high-tide mark and about half a mile long. Between
the sea and the farm was a stretch of swamp country, full of
raupo, cabbage trees and flax bushes. The place was completely
exposed to the prevailing north-westerly winds and the few
patches of manuka scrub that survived were stunted and wind-
clipped. Nothing grew tall there.

There was no beach where the swamp met the sea, it went
straight out onto the mudflats, with a straggly row of small
mangroves along the water's edge, and there was no actual
outlet from the swamp out onto the mudflats, it just seeped. On
spring tides the water backed up in the drains and overflowed
into the paddocks.

The old two-bedroomed house and a shed stood on a slight
rise out in one of the paddocks. A corrugated-iron fence had
been erected along one side of the house for a windbreak. It was

brown with rust and rattled in the wind. The cowshed further over was a rusty iron affair on a pad of crumbling concrete, set in a sea of mud. The place was supposed to be two hundred and fifty acres but half of it was swamp and the other half was boggy. You couldn't walk anywhere on it without gumboots.

Day and night the whole area was filled with the croaking of frogs, untold thousands of them. The other main sounds on Mudflat Farm were the pukekos kicking up a racket in the raupo. There were hundreds of pukekos and morning and evening they'd spread out across the paddocks, pricking their way through the bulrushy lime-deficient pasture, probably eating more grass than the cows did. Our old man reckoned that Mudflat was carrying thirty pukekos and half a cow to the acre.

This, then, was Mudflat Farm when the Duggan brothers, nephews of old Charlie, took it over. They arrived one dirty day in June when it was raining and blowing half a gale, with their possessions under a flapping tarpaulin on the back of an old three-ton Bedford truck. They made it halfway across the paddock to the house before the truck sank to its axles in the boggy ground. It stayed where it was right through the May school holidays until there was a bit of a dry spell and they dug it out and snigged it back up onto the road with their rusty old Ferguson tractor.

Everyone around was waiting to see if the Duggan brothers were going to be able to make a go of it. Arthur and Billy, both in their mid-twenties, but they obviously knew a bit about farming.

Mudflat Farm was badly run-down and neglected. The first thing that needed doing was the fences. They stripped one stretch of broken-down fence to get the materials to patch other broken-down stretches with, and in a few weeks they'd done all they could with what they had and their boundary fences were temporarily semi-secure.

With no income until the cows came into production in a couple of months, they were going to have to live off the land as much as possible. There were rabbits on the higher ground above the road on our place and they ate rabbit a couple of times a week. They could hook an eel out of the swamp any time they wanted one and they found that the flounder net was nearly always good for a feed of flats or herrings when they found the time to stick it out.

The odd grey duck was a good stand-by in lean times, and they found quite a few duck and black-swan nests around the edges of the swamp. They discovered that they could work all day on a couple of slices of bread made with duck eggs. The swans' eggs were so rich that one of them was a feed and they could only eat them occasionally.

The sixty cows were heavy in calf and in poor condition. There was half a pit of ensilage left and they fed it out as sparingly as they dared, but it was going to run out on them. They put the cows out on the road for a few hours each day when it wasn't raining, to graze what they could off the roadsides. They had a paddock closed up for emergencies but there wasn't much grass growth in it. In short, no one could see how they were going to make it through the winter.

They cleaned out some of the drains that ran through the paddocks into the swamp but it didn't make any difference. The water still backed up in the drains at high tide, and sometimes overflowed into the paddocks. They decided to put a drain through a part of the swamp and possibly dry out some of the paddocks. It had to be done by hand because any machine would have sunk to the axles before it could get near where they wanted to drain.

They started digging with spade and shovel where the swamp seeped out onto the mudflats, but every shovelful they took out immediately filled up with stagnant water. They were making a puddle.

Further into the swamp they cut the floating weed with a sharpened hay-knife and dragged the clumps out with a swamp-hook. The result of this was another stagnant puddle. The ducks enjoyed it. The Duggan brothers gave up trying to drain their swamp; with no fall there was nowhere for the water to drain away to.

For all the water they were living up to their hocks in, the actual water supply to the farm was very unreliable. It came from a small dam in a creek above the road on our place, through a one-inch pipe that passed through a culvert under the road and into a four-hundred-gallon tank. The dam kept silting up and they were always having to go up there in the rain and clear it and get the pipe running again.

They bogged on through the winter and on a filthy night when the rain hammered onto the roof so hard that you had to almost shout to make yourself heard, their first two calves were born. One of them drowned in a puddle before it got onto its feet. The other one survived, as did fifty-two others, and the Duggan brothers began to get a little income off the place. First the bobby-calf cheques and then the few dollars a day they got for the milk. Most of the income had to be used to buy stock food to keep the cows going until they got some spring growth, which was late that year.

The milk tanker got stuck in their paddock and they couldn't budge it with their tractor, so they got the Ministry of Works grader to have a try and that got stuck as well. Once you broke through the surface of that ground you were into porridge. They had to bring a log-hauler from miles away to winch them out and the Duggans had to get the driveway metalled before they'd bring the tanker in again. Another unforeseen expense.

This, then, was Mudflat Farm when the Duggan brothers had been farming it for a year. The total income had been less than one person's wages and the expenditures had been somewhat more than that, but they weren't giving up.

It was only after they'd had proved they could handle the conditions that the locals began to seriously help them with gear, work and advice, and things were a lot easier for them after that. (Our old man used to say that unless they proved that they had the necessary gills it was no use trying to help them.)

Everyone pitched in and gave them a hand to get hay and ensilage in for the winter. The old man lent them our pedigree Jersey bull so they could get a bit of improvement in their herd. A bunch of them got together and put in a concrete race and an extra yard on their cowshed so they wouldn't be working in so much mud. They helped them with netting and posts so they could grow a vegetable garden for themselves and not for the wekas. Fred Murray leased them some winter grazing and they were able to increase the number of their cows to a hundred, which was agreed was the minimum they needed to make the place worth working.

About three years after the Duggan brothers arrived we moved away to a farm in another more productive district. By this time they were actually making a living off Mudflat Farm. Us kids even made a bit of pocket money, spreading fertiliser and grass seed by hand and pulling ragwort and digging rushes for them. They'd bought the runoff they'd been leasing and increased their milking herd to a hundred and twenty cows and everyone around liked and respected them. They had what it took.

That was fairly typical of how the pioneers were able to bring much of the marginal country into production, hard work and co-operation with each other. I wonder where all that went, I haven't seen those things around for years now.

2

THE BLACK BOAR

He wasn't especially big, as wild boars go. About two hundred pounds' weight in his prime. Over the years he'd been seen many times in our valley and the one further over that backed onto the National Park, but his main stamping ground was the high bushed ridge at the back of our place.

The local hunters all knew about the Black Boar and they'd been onto him with their dogs many times, but no one had ever stopped him for long. He was known to have a good set of tusks on him and he'd bail for long enough to carve up a dog or two and then take off down one of the long bush spurs and lose the dogs in a big area of swamp and tangled supplejack and toitoi and kiekie in the bottom of the valley.

Most of the pig hunters didn't carry guns, they relied on their dogs to hold the pigs by their ears until they could get there and deal to them with a pig-sticker, which was often a cut-down and sharpened bayonet. No one had got quite near enough to the Black Boar to use one of them on him.

He was cheeky. He'd been spotted down around the road, out in the paddocks, in the gully behind our woolshed, on walking tracks and bush roads. You could run into him just about anywhere around there. Quite a few hunters had got a shot at him, some even claiming to have winged him, but he was still around.

One of his lurks was to hang around near a mob of other pigs and if the dogs got onto him he'd bolt through the pigs and the dogs would usually take off after one of the others and he'd be away again. He sometimes did the same thing with mobs of goats feeding on the ferny faces.

Once when there was a pighunting competition with a five-hundred-dollar prize for the heaviest boar they took three packs of dogs up there to try and get him, but not long after they'd left the road the boar came down across the road, ran past some people having a picnic on the riverbank, splashed through the river and disappeared into the fern on the other side of the valley. Another time he walked right past two blokes who were trout fishing and wandered across the road bridge as though he knew how harmless their trout rods were.

Two hunters with four dogs knocked him up in a scrubby gully one day and he ran round the side of the hill and forced his way under a deer fence into the paddock and the dogs couldn't get through it to get at him. The last they saw of him he was trotting toward the far side of the deer paddock, where he lifted a post out of the ground and got out under the fence and crossed our ridge paddock and away into the bush.

The Black Boar was credited with having killed a lot of dogs and wounded many more. At one stage they were carrying ripped dogs out of the bush almost every weekend. He was no doubt blamed for many missing dogs he'd had nothing to do with, but his actual known tally was impressive enough for any boar.

My brother and I were mustering sheep down off our back paddock one day and we surprised the Black Boar out of a patch of fern near the top of the ridge. He took off up the hill and we heard him hit the boundary fence just out of sight from us. We went up there and found that he'd broken three wires of the fence and gone into the bush on the other side of the ridge. We had to cart some gear up there and fix the hole he'd made in the fence.

Another time I remember we were heading into town, all dressed up and crammed into the Land-Rover, and we came around a corner and there was the Black Boar standing in the middle of the road. We stopped. It doesn't pay to try and ram a wild pig with a motor vehicle, it's like running into a lump of rock. The boar ran towards us and then dived up a track that went up a bank on the top side of the road and vanished. It was as though he knew when you didn't have any guns or dogs with you.

He scared hell out of our mother and sister one day. Mum used to make the best blackberry jelly in the world to spread on the best scones ever made. They were picking blackberries along the riverbank and carried a nine-inch-wide board about eight feet long that they used to lay on the blackberry clumps so they could walk into them and get at the fruit. They threw their board onto a clump of blackberry and the Black Boar exploded out of it with a loud WHOOF! We heard their screams from over at the woolshed, where we were docking lambs. He was having a snore-off in the blackberries while they were hunting for him up in the bush.

Some of the pig hunters deliberately went after the Black Boar with their big bully dogs, determined to nail his hide to the wall of their shed. Others were hunting for pork and didn't want their dogs ripped up and tried to keep out of his way, and yet, strangely enough, they seemed to get onto him more often than the ones who were looking for him. The end result was always the same, the dogs got beaten up and the pig got away. Just about every large black boar caught around there was claimed to be the Black Boar, but he continued to avoid the bullet, the bayonet and the hangi-pit.

Every now and again he seemed to be gone and wouldn't be sighted or got onto for weeks, or even months. They used to say he'd probably been caught, shot or died of old age, and then someone would get onto him and it would be all on again.

He was still around when I left home and went shooting deer for a living in the southern mountains. It was more than three years before I returned home on a visit. The old farm was still ticking over.

One day I decided to go up the back and knock off a goat for the farm dogs because we were out of dog tucker. I took my brother's new .30-06 Winchester rifle with a 7x-power Zeiss telescopic sight. I'd been using nothing but the old Lee Enfield .303 army rifle with open sights, a good gun, but this one of my brother's was the Rolls-Royce of guns to me and I was looking forward to having a go with it.

It was a hot day and as I climbed the ridge toward a mob of goats I'd spotted through the scope I decided to take a breather and sat in a soft clump of fern on the crest of the spur.

As I sat there looking around the old familiar scene I caught a movement out of the corner of my eye and looked around, and there in the gully below me was what I first thought might be a black goat or a calf, walking along a sheep and goat track around the steep face of the hill. Then I saw that it was a pig. It looked like the Black Boar.

I sank slowly into the fern and wriggled on my stomach down the slope until I was behind a rise in the ground. I poked the rifle over the mound and sighted on him through the scope. It was him all right, the Black Boar himself, mooching along in the hot sun, slapping the stump of his tail lazily from side to side. I hadn't heard he was still around.

Through the scope I could see his tattered ears and the scars of fights criss-crossed on his old hide. He was almost grey with age and I could clearly see a big silver scar across the three-inch-thick shield of hide on his shoulder and the white sneer of the tusk and grinder on his jaw.

It was an easy shot. He was side-on at seventy-five yards and moving slow. I worked the bolt and slid a round into the breech and lined the cross-hairs up on the point of his shoulder where his neck joined his body and steadied my aim, touched my finger to the hair-trigger that would send the 180-grain silver-tipped bullet mushrooming into him at around three thousand feet a second.

I couldn't do it. You can call me soft if you like, but I just couldn't do it. I'd have blown away any other pig or any deer or any goat I could have got lined up on without giving it a second thought, but I just couldn't execute the old Black Boar like that.

Somehow it would have been a cowardly act and to this day I'm glad I didn't do it.

Just to keep the old boy on his toes I lowered my aim and fired, blowing a rock to bits right underneath his belly. He took off and by the time the tearing echo of the shot had faded from the surrounding hills he was out of sight around the face. He still had plenty of go in him, I wouldn't have got a second shot in.

I never saw the Black Boar again and never heard of anyone nailing him. I hope he died peacefully of old age. I reckoned he'd earned that.

3

THE REAL
THING

At one part of it I was working for a cow cocky in the Waikato and one day he asked me if I'd mind looking after his brother-in-law's farm while he and his wife and daughter went away for a fortnight's holiday. I didn't mind, a change being as good as a rest. The brother-in-law came and collected me and took me to their farm out Raglan way. I was to stay with them for a few days before they left, to get the hang of what needed doing.

It was your average sort of dairy farm, two hundred acres, old house and buildings, three-wire fences, an eight-bail cowshed and muddy races and gateways. The cows were dried off for the winter and all I had to do was feed out and shift the stock around a bit. I also had to feed the pigs, the dogs, the chooks, the ducks and the cat.

Things went smoothly for the first ten days. I was right on top of the work and had plenty of spare time and there were a lot of books in the house I hadn't read. It was almost cushy.

I was sitting in an armchair in front of the electric heater one day reading a book when a taxi pulled up at the gate and a middle-aged couple got out and came up to the house. They said they were expected and where could they put their stuff. They had three large suitcases and two smaller bags.

The brother-in-law had told me, several times, that he was getting this couple in to take over share-milking the cows next season. They must have got their dates mixed up. Well they were here now, we were just going to have to make the best of it until the brother-in-law got back from his holiday in four days' time. They paid off the taxi and I gave them a hand to put their cases in a two-roomed cottage out in the paddock. It wasn't much of a share-milker's house. It had two single beds with lumpy kapok mattresses, a table and three chairs, a leaking sofa and one armchair. Their stove was a two-element electric caravan job sitting on one end of the sink bench. There was a dead possum in one of the cupboards. I apologised for the state of the place but they didn't seem to mind what they called 'roughing it'. They were Dutch with heavy accents and it was a bit hard to understand their talk.

I found them some linen and blankets around the house and a pair of gumboots each and got them more or less settled in. We agreed that they would eat and wash at the main house until the brother-in-law arrived home and got them properly organised.

It didn't take long to discover that the brother-in-law's new sharemilkers didn't know much about farming. They didn't know how to lift a bale of hay, and they couldn't drive the tractor. I had to do everything myself until they'd mastered the delicate art of chucking biscuits of hay off the trailer. There was a snorty old Jersey bull in the bull paddock and the couple were so nervous of him they wouldn't go near the fence he was behind to throw some hay over. When I stopped to open up a drain that was blocked they just stood there and watched. The Mrs was so scared of the pigs she wouldn't go near the pigsty, otherwise they stuck together almost nervously.

I would have expected the woman to have got stuck in and sort their cottage out, but she came everywhere around the farm, all three of us together. I wasn't used to working like that. She even brought a camera on the second day and took a whole roll of film of us feeding out. She left most of the cooking and cleaning-up to her old man and me.

I started getting impatient with these two. They were making more work than they were saving, and they were helping themselves to the brother-in-law's booze, which I thought was a bit presumptuous of them.

After breakfast on the third day we went out to load up the feed. I'd decided to feed ensilage that day and when I'd got it loaded the bloke said he didn't think they'd be able to come and feed out with me today, they had some letter writing to catch up on, and I told him he could bloody well feed the bloody pigs before he did anything else, and she could at least chuck a bit of grain to the chooks and ducks and bring the bloody eggs in, upon which I hopped on the tractor and took off to feed out on my own, only too pleased not to have those two hanging around me.

I knew something was wrong when I was still up in the back paddock. The dogs tied up down at the house were barking their heads off. I hurried through the job and when I got back to the house the Mrs was standing in the yard covered in mud and over in the paddock the Mr was chasing pigs around the paddock with a stick.

What had happened was, she'd fed the chooks but when she went to get the eggs from the nesting boxes the rooster took to her and she got a fright and ran round the back of the cowshed into a foot of sloshy mud. The gumboots she was wearing were too big for her and one of her feet came out of the boot and into the mud, whereupon she lost balance and both hands went into the mud as well. By the time she'd floundered her way out of there she was in a right old mess. She was wearing white slacks and pink socks. She stood there with her hands held out like a shag drying its wings, demanding to know what she was going to do about this.

Her old man, in the meantime, had dropped a bucket into the pig pen when he was feeding them and, being a man of resourcefulness, he opened the shutter and let the pigs out into the big pen so he could retrieve the bucket. Unfortunately he hadn't noticed that there was another gate open and the pigs ran straight through the yard and out into the paddock.

I got two buckets with a bit of pig tucker in each and the pigs all followed me back into the pen with them. Then I got the Mrs washed down with the cowshed hose and she went off to have a bath and change her clothes without even saying thanks.

While the Mrs was having her bath the Mr and I sat in the kitchen having a cup of tea. He said he didn't think that they'd be staying there and I said I didn't think so either. Then the Mrs came out of the bathroom with an armful of mud-stained clothes, still looking a bit disgruntled, and told me in her broken English that they were going to have to have a word with my boss about my inhospitable behaviour. They were welcome, I was going to have a word with him myself, about how useless they were around the place. There was no way those two were ever going to manage a dairy herd.

They went off to their cottage and I didn't see them for the rest of the day. They came over to the house that night asking me when their dinner was. I slapped up a hash for them and the next day they didn't even come out of their cottage when I did the feeding out. In fact they weren't even talking to me by this time, it had become a standoff.

That afternoon the brother-in-law and his wife and daughter arrived back from their holiday. I was glad to see them, I'd had just about enough of their new share-milkers. The brother-in-law wanted to know who those people coming over from the cottage were and when I told him he said he'd never heard of them. He hadn't even advertised the share-milking job yet. There'd obviously been some sort of misunderstanding going on.

It took quite a bit of explaining and sorting out, that lot. The Dutch couple were never supposed to have been there in the first place. They'd booked a week's farmstay holiday with the brother-in-law's brother who lived in the big old family homestead a mile back down the road. They'd come to the wrong Harris place.

The Dutch couple spent the rest of their holiday in the luxury of the big homestead down the road, but I'd be willing to bet they remembered the first part of their homestay holiday longer than the second. After all, you can't beat the real thing, can you.

4
THE POST

They reckon life begins at forty, but as far as I'm concerned the most interesting age was fourteen because that meant I was nearly fifteen and at fifteen you were allowed to leave school and get on with your life. As my fifteenth birthday approached I worked out how much I could jump the gun by to avoid the attentions of any truant officers who might take an interest in my case, and with about four months to go I mounted the trusty bicycle I'd paid off at ten bob a week working in a factory and delivering papers outside school hours and with the rest of my worldly possessions in a sugar bag I left the family home near Auckland and pedalled off down the old Great South Road on the first leg of the journey that brought me to this point. I haven't been all that chuffed about one or two of the things that have happened along the way – but I digress.

About thirty miles down the Great South Road, not a long ride for me in those days (in fact I doubled a girl about ten miles of it on the bar of my bike; she was going to visit her boyfriend at the Papakura Military Camp), I saw this small dairy farm, just south of Drury. On an impulse I turned up the driveway and found a bloke standing outside a house calling a dog which didn't seem to be anywhere around. I asked him if he needed a good farm hand and he didn't know, but he took me inside and introduced me to his wife and they gave me a cup of tea and some bread and jam.

It was about four o'clock in the afternoon and the boss

announced that he'd better go and get the cows in. I'll do that for you, I said, I've got nothing else to do. He hesitated and then nodded.

The farm was obvious. The cows were in the paddock, the milking shed was there and all set up. I'd been milking in various cowsheds since my hands were too small to put the cups on them. I had these ones in the yard and the right cows went into the right bails in the right order and I did most of them on my own. My new boss helped a bit and told me how he went about things and before you knew it the cows were in the night paddock, the shed cleaned up, chops and mashed spuds for dinner and a bed in my own room. I had my first job.

We found his dog, by the way. It was a beautiful big English Setter and it had been in the boot of his car for two days.

Within a few weeks I was more part of the family than I could have imagined. There were just the boss, his wife and me on the place and it was a breeze to keep the farm ticking over. My first boss and his wife were two of the nicest people I've ever known – but I digress again, this yarn is supposed to be about a post. I know it sounds a bit odd but I was quite fond of this particular post.

There was an old bloke called Dave who did work for farmers around the district and between milkings I helped him renew some of the fences on our place. One of the first things we had to do was cut down a big sprawling eighty-year-old macrocarpa tree and cut our posts out of it. No treated pine in those days. We rubbed our way through this tree with a cross-cut saw and felled it. A great tangle of branches and heads out in the paddock. We cut all the posts we could get out of the branches and then started splitting them out of the trunk with a splitting gun, a tapered hollow cast-iron tube which was filled with black blasting powder and hammered into the end of the log with a maul. Then a fuse was inserted into a hole in it and lit. If you were lucky the explosion split the log.

The macrocarpa was stringy and twisted and it was hard work wedging and axing the posts out of it. Finally we trimmed a big strainer out of the heartwood. Eight feet long and two feet square. Dave believed in building things to last.

We started on a new dividing fence. There'd been a long spell of hot dry weather and the brown clay ground was baked as hard as concrete. While Dave took the first grassy spit out of the post holes I went along with cream cans full of water on the horse-drawn sledge and poured buckets of water into the holes. Then we loosened the clay in the bottom of the holes with a crowbar and inched them deeper.

Then the big strainer. It took the two of us half a day to dig the hole for it, down on our boundary near the main road. It weighed several hundredweight and we levered it onto the sledge with poles and took it down there and after wiring a block of heartwood onto it for a foot we up-ended it into the hole we'd dug. A few inches at a time we spaded the clay into the hole around the post and rammed it until the rammer rang. By the time the hole was half full old Dave reckoned we could have strained the fence off it. By milking time it was finished. While I went to get the cows in Dave cut a square out of a sheet of corrugated iron and nailed it over the top of our post to keep the water out of it.

We chiselled slots in our post and put in stays, though they weren't really necessary. We strained fences three ways off that post. It wasn't going to move.

I stayed on that job for about ten months and then headed south for the bush, and over the years whenever I passed that way in a variety of different vehicles I naturally always looked across the farm where I'd had my first job and always checked that the post was still there. Even after a long spell of contract fencing I still had a bit of pride in that post.

In the intervening years I did a lot of fencing. I put fences up ridges so steep we had to dig footholds in the side of the hill so we could stand there and dig the holes and ram the posts sideways into the ground. I put fences in rock where we had to jackhammer the holes and drive in standards. I worked on fences in swamps and across mudflats. I cemented posts into crevices in rock, but I never had the satisfaction that went with having put that magnificent macrocarpa post in with old Dave beside the Great South Road in 1952.

The farm changed hands, two new lots of fences were strained off our post. The motorway was put in and the old Great South Road was by-passed at that point and formed a loop a hundred yards from the motorway. The post still stood there like the immovable object, streaked with grey and red lichens.

Finally, after more than forty years, they divided the land up into housing sections and my post was suddenly gone and now when I pass that way I wonder how they got it out of the ground. Probably with one of those digging machines you see everywhere around these days.

That post of ours certainly outlasted old Dave and the bloke who paid us to put it there, and if it had been left alone it would have most likely outlasted me as well. In fact I'd be willing to bet that if it had been left alone that chunk of macrocarpa heartwood would have withstood the ravages of time and the many tons of constant strain pulling off it for a hundred years. Some post, that!

5

HARD
YAKKER

When I was a young bloke knocking around the country, working somewhere for a while and then moving on somewhere else, I ran into some hard-case bosses, but one that stands out in my memory was an old bloke called Jesse. He was what you might call 'Hard Yakker'.

I was almost broke again so I answered an ad in a newspaper that said they wanted a single teamster. Four pound ten a week and your keep. I got the bloke on the phone and he sounded a bit abrupt but he told me he'd give me a go and the best way to get out to his place was with the Rural Delivery bloke who carried paying passengers.

Late the next day the RD van deposited me at the gate of a real primitive farm, miles from anywhere. It was a very untidy place, to say the least. There was wire and timber and sheets of iron and drums and old bits of machinery and junk scattered around all over the place. The house was two old army huts joined together. There was a tumble-down harness shed and another shed out in the stumpy paddock where a dozen draught horses stood around a pile of hay.

As I approached the house I could see that there'd once been a garden around it but they'd let the horses in to keep the grass down and now you could only see where the garden had been. There was no one around. The back door was open and I looked into the kitchen. The floor mats and curtains were hessian superphosphate sacks. The tablecloth was newspaper. There were a couple of dented pots and a chipped enamel plate and mug on the wooden sink bench. There was a black streak up the wall behind the electric stove where it had been on fire. Through in the other room I could see the rumpled blankets and trailing grey sheets of a grubby unmade bed. Whoever lived here lived rough and lived alone.

I left my bag on the porch and went for a look around. The boss wasn't hard to find, he was down the paddock blowing stumps with gelignite. He was a stocky little old bloke with a weather-beaten face under a big hat and he was covered with dirt and black from the stumps he'd been blowing. He shook hands and told me his name was Jesse and he'd be coming up to the house shortly, which was fairly predictable since it was getting dark by this time. He let go the charge he was preparing and blew a big matai stump loose in the ground. Then we went up to the house to get me settled in.

Jesse said he'd got a shack rigged up for me to sleep in over by the house. I hadn't noticed any shack there. It turned out to be an old shed in a bit of a hollow thirty yards from the house. He lent me a torch to go and put my stuff in it while he 'slapped up a feed'.

My new quarters turned out to be an old fowl house, not quite high enough to stand up straight in. Two chaff sacks threaded on poles was the bunk. There was a candle on a wooden box beside the bunk and a set of drawers with half the handles missing leaned against one wall. The floor was dirt, the place stank of mouldy fowl house and the only opening was the doorway. There was no door but Jesse had pointed out an old wooden ramp I could always lean over the doorway if the wind started blowing the rain in. I sat my bag and myself on the bunk and looked around with the torch. There was a hole in one corner where the rats had been coming in and out.

As I went back to the house to join my new boss for a feed I was beginning to wonder what I'd come amongst. I'd camped in places as rough as that, but only from necessity. In fact that had to be the very roughest accommodation I'd ever known to be provided for a farm worker.

Jesse's tucker turned out to be as rough as his accommodation. That night's dinner was two sausages burnt on the outside and raw in the middle, two boiled spuds and bread and butter. The tea had tealeaves and lumps of powdered milk floating in it. When I went to spear another potato out of the pot he said, "Leave them spuds, boy. I'm gunna fry 'em up for breakfast." So I had another slice of bread instead.

Over this rather frugal repast Jesse informed me that he'd been advertising for a housekeeper but 'none a' the bitches'd take it on'. The last one hadn't even got out of the RD van. He couldn't figure out what was wrong with them. He had the bloody power on, didn't he?

I didn't sleep too well that night, partly because of the narrow sagging bunk, partly because a loose sheet of iron on the roof was rapping in the wind, and partly because the place was infested with fleas. I was woken from a fitful doze by a loud crash on the roof, then another. It was old Jesse throwing rocks from up at the house to wake me up. It was still dark. I lit my candle.

"Get the horses in and come up for a feed," he yelled out.

"Okay," I yelled back.

Finding a dozen strange horses in a strange paddock in the dark has never been easy and it was starting to get daylight by the time I had them in the yard. When I got up to the house Jesse wanted to know what the hell I'd been doing. I'd gone and made us late getting started.

After a breakfast as uninspired as last night's dinner Jesse said he'd give me a hand to harness the team the first time. Seeing as we were using a six-horse team in the chain-blocks it was a good idea. You need to know which collar and harness goes on which horse and where each horse goes in the team. It's a major part of teamstering and important to get it right.

Like many other new farms in those days, the whole place had been clear-felled and burnt off. We were dragging the blackened logs and stumps into heaps with the horses, getting the place ready to be disced up and planted in grass. Jesse loosened the stumps with gelignite, blowing them to bits if they were too stubborn, and I snigged them into a gully with the team. They were good horses and I soon got the hang of them. It was very dirty work and we were soon both black from the mud and the burnt stumps and logs we were handling. Logs that were too big for the horses to shift we'd rub our way through with a blunt M-tooth saw.

It was well into the afternoon and the horses needed a spell so Jesse reluctantly agreed that we might as well knock off for lunch. I wasn't expecting anything sumptuous, I was so hungry I would have eaten just about anything, but when he got a loaf of bread wrapped in newspaper out of the lunch bag and broke a hunk off it and started eating it I could only stand and stare at him.

"Here," he said, poking the loaf towards me. "Have some of that."

I tore off a piece of bread and chewed on it.

"Not much of a lunch, Boss," I ventured.

"It's all you need," he said. "It's all I ever have."

"Have we got anything to drink?" I asked.

"Plenty of water in the creek there," he said.

We worked until we lost the light and I unharnessed and fed the horses in the dark, while Jesse went ahead up to the house to slap a feed on. I had a wash at the tap outside and went into the house, where Jesse dished up dinner. Two boiled eggs each with slices of bread and butter.

"Is this dinner?" I said.

"Yeah. It's all we got until the RD van gets here with the grocery order tomorrow. Don't eat too much bread, it's got to do us for breakfast in the morning. I'm not used to havin' to feed so many."

I went to bed hungry that night but I was so tired the fleas didn't even keep me awake. I slept right through until the rocks started landing on the roof.

Old Jesse worked me from daylight until dark and fed me miserable, unappetising little feeds. I had to shuffle the horses around because some of them weren't standing up to the work as well as others. It started pouring with rain one day, you could tell it was going to rain before we started. I waited to see when Jesse was going to knock off, but no show. If you could see, you worked. No point in knocking off just for a bit of rain.

We ended up wet, filthy and cold that night and over a watery feed of boiled cabbage and rice I enquired about the possibility of having a hot bath. I was out of luck, the bath was the one out in the paddock that we fed the horses oats and chaff in. The hot water system wasn't working at the moment so I heated some water on the stove and had a bath in a basin out in the paddock in the rain. To top off a bad day the roof over my bunk leaked and my sleeping bag was wet.

Young blokes had more respect for old blokes in those days and you didn't question too much injustice, but after ten days of constant slogging I was ready to ask Jesse some pertinent questions, like when I was going to get a day off, when I was going to get paid, and what about a decent feed? (We'd been eating onions with every meal because Jesse had found a couple of bad ones in the bag and wanted to get them eaten before any more went off.) The answers to my questions were,

"What do you want days off for? There's nothing to do round here except work." "You'll have to wait until I go into town to get you some pay," and "I don't believe in wasting good grub."

"When do you think you'll be going into town?" I enquired.

"Dunno," he said. "I was in there two or three weeks ago. There's nothin' to do there anyway."

"There's my money," I pointed out.

"You don't need money out here," he said. "There's nothin' to spend it on."

"But I need a new pair of boots," I said desperately. "And some clothes. I've only got one pair of strides that aren't ripped."

"We'll get you some next time we have to go into town for somethin'," he said.

The bloke was preposterous. I could have gone to the union over him, if I'd been a member. I couldn't move on until I got paid, so I had a pair of boots sent out on the Rural Delivery and stuck it out for another month, during which time I got half a day off to do some washing.

Jesse dished up some hard-case feeds. I would have preferred to take over the cooking but I couldn't find anything to cook. I didn't have Jesse's imagination. Who else but him would cut a pumpkin into three hunks and boil it in a pot and dish it up half cooked with bread and butter, one hunk for him, one hunk for me and the other hunk for breakfast in the morning. When I declined his offer to pour some golden syrup over some boiled spuds he'd served up he suggested some condensed milk instead. He wasn't being frugal, he was just being himself. He'd been brought up frugal and never known anything else, but I saw no good reason why I should suffer for it.

Finally Jesse had to go to town on some business or other so I took the opportunity to go with him and tell him I was chucking the job in. He didn't seem surprised that I was going, he was used to that I guess. The trip into town in his old 1929 Essex car was a hair-raising experience but we made it, and we were the scruffiest-looking pair on the street. I waited around outside his accountant's office for a fair while until Jesse finally came out and handed me twenty-three pounds in notes. I counted it.

"This is only twenty-three quid," I said. "I figure you owe me twenty-seven quid."

"I had to deduct a bit of tax," he said. "And there was that day you didn't work. I'm not payin' a man not to work."

"What about my holiday pay?" I said.

He glared at me as though I'd lost my marbles and said, "I don't pay anyone to go on holiday."

He was too much. I gave up and walked away from him.

By the time I'd got myself back into roughly the same sort of shape I'd been in before I started working for old Jesse (e.g. a huge feed of steak and eggs with all the trimmings, some new

36

clothes, a hot bath and a night in a proper bed), I had fifteen quid left of my wages. I'd been through all that work and privation for two pounds ten a week. Five bucks!

I was a bit less trusting of any bosses I took on after that but mercifully I've never run into another one as miserable to work for as old Jesse. Hard yakker, that.

6
SHIRAZ

I'd never had anything to do with Arab horses until I had one given to me. My niece pulled up with this thing in a horse float. A little white stallion, pure-bred, three years old, not fully broken in. He was called Shiraz.

I thanked my niece and put Shiraz in the paddock. He was a skittery little thing to handle. I thought that maybe we could gentle it down for the kids to ride.

It was a month or so before I got round to riding Shiraz. He was sluggish and sulky and had an uncomfortable gait. I stuck him back in the paddock and left him there for the time being. I didn't put him in with the other horses because half of them were mares and I wasn't sure that I wanted any half-Arab foals around.

It was winter and I threw a bit of hay over the fence for Shiraz each day, and after a while he started getting friendly. Followed me around whenever I was in his paddock and put on a performance for me, rearing and prancing and swinging his head around and generally carrying on. He even got to calling out whenever he saw me and prancing up and down the fence. I made a bit of a fuss of him, it's hard not to when an animal gets that matey with you.

I rode Shiraz again one day when my good mare was lame and he was a different horse from the first time. Smooth and fast and easy to control. He liked to get in front of the other horses and stay there. Although he was green he insisted on leading the way up a two-thousand-foot climb. We mustered cattle up there all day and by the time we got them down to the holding paddock that night Shiraz was dead beat but still keen to go. There was nothing of him but he sure had guts and stamina.

I got to riding Shiraz most of the time. He didn't like me riding anything else, kicked up a hell of a stink if I did. I think he was even a bit jealous of my dogs. He was a good stock-horse. Once he knew where you wanted them he wouldn't let them go anywhere else. I never had to catch him or tie him up, he just stuck around where I was.

One day I was up the back of the farm and Shiraz was hanging around so I decided to ride him back to the house. I got a piece of baling twine off the fence and called Shiraz over and made a crude halter and hopped on him, ready to hop off again if he bolted on me. But he handled like a lamb. He'd never liked having a bit put in his mouth and I never used one on him again, only a hackamore with a single rein after that.

He was a bit of a nuisance at times with the fuss he made when I didn't ride him. He demanded attention, more like a dog than a horse in some ways, but his other attributes more than compensated for that. I never had to catch him, he was always there. He enjoyed working, especially stock work, the harder the better. He thrived on it. In fact he was turning into a bit of a show-off.

Shiraz had been my main horse for about eighteen months when a couple of my mates asked if I could give them a hand to get six hundred steers through the old Silver Hill Road. This road was no longer used for traffic. There were several bad slips on it and rather than fix them they'd bulldozed a big ridge of earth across it at either end and closed the road to all traffic. These mates of mine were driving their cattle over the Silver Hill to fatten them. There was hock-deep grass along the sides of the road and if you let the cattle feed their way along for a week or two to top them up you could get them to the sale in prime condition. I'd taken cattle through there once before so they asked me to lend a hand.

The first bit was easy. The road wound its way up a valley and all we had to do was walk behind the cattle as they fed their way along. Three mounted men and ten dogs seemed too much to control the six hundred head of stock, which were fairly quiet anyway. We camped the cattle on the road at night and ourselves under a tarpaulin we carried on a pack horse with all our other gear and our tucker.

The other blokes slung off a bit about my horse at first. Stallions aren't usually welcome on a droving job because they can disrupt the other horses.

"That pony is too small for you, Crumpy. You want to get yourself something with a bit of grunt in it."

"I've got enough grunt under me," I replied.

In five days we were near the top of the Silver Hill ridge, native bush each side of the road, which fell off steeply on one side. We'd filed the cattle through a couple of places where most of the road had slipped away and they were getting used to it. We'd also had to cut through several trees that had fallen across the road, but we were pleased enough with the progress we were making and there was plenty of grass for the cattle.

Then one afternoon the cattle started backing up on us so one of the blokes rode through them to see what was holding them up and found we'd come to a place where the whole road had slipped away. The goats and deer had trodden a track in the shingle ten yards across the slip to the road on the other side. He led his horse across and the cattle started to follow in single file.

It took a couple of hours, we didn't dare to push them too hard, and we only had sixty more to get across when the track gave way under the punishment it was taking and first one steer and then another slithered and rolled forty yards down the shingle and floundered into a jumble of boulders at the bottom. The cattle behind tried to jump across the gap and broke more track away and down they went. The others followed, the whole sixty of them. There were cattle falling on top of cattle down there in a struggling bellowing tangle.

This was a disaster. The chances of us being able to get those cattle out of there were obviously very slim indeed. It was going to be a huge loss.

As it turned out there was no need to decide what to do about it. There wasn't even time to decide whether to be a hero or not. As the last of the cattle fell down the slip Shiraz wanted to go after them and head them off, so I let him. He launched us over the edge and we slid down the slide the cattle had made, sitting on his haunches. I could only lay back on his rump and hang on. I remember still the rattling of the stones and the grunting of the horse as we jolted and plunged down that crazy slope.

After what seemed a long time we reached the bottom still hanging together and crashed into a cattle beast, knocking it off another one it was on top of. I went flying through the air and landed on stones. The horse had all four feet in the air. I'd just stood up when a rock we'd dislodged came bowling down the slope and clouted me on the ankle. I felt something give and landed on the stones again.

We all struggled to our feet, the horse, the cattle and me, and there we were, standing around in the bush at the bottom of this slip. Even my two dogs wouldn't come down the way we had and went running down the road to find a way round.

I hobbled across and leaned on Shiraz. There was definitely something wrong with my ankle, I couldn't take any weight on it at all. I was bruised and grazed in quite a few places but the ankle was the worst. The horse was okay, though, which was the main thing.

Calling out up and down the slip we arranged that I'd have a go at driving the cattle up through the bush and try and get them out onto the road, while the other blokes dug a new track across the slip. There were only about three hours of daylight left so we got on with it.

I got on my horse and started dogging and chasing the cattle through the bush, letting them pick the best way along deer and pig and goat tracks across the steep face. There was a rifle shot.

One of the steers had broken a front leg and the blokes had got the gun from the packhorse and shot it from the top of the slip. Amazingly that was our only casualty apart from a few patches of hide left on the rocks at the bottom of the slip.

It was slow going, easing those cattle through the bush trying to keep them more or less together and angling upwards towards the road in the hope of finding a place where we could get up on to it. Scrambling through running rock and slippery creek-heads. I could get off the horse and stand on one leg to disentangle him from the vines, but I had to get back on him to move anywhere. I couldn't walk.

It was getting dark. We'd been moving along under the road for about an hour without finding any way up. The first indication I had that we'd found a track out onto the road was when I noticed the mob was thinning out. Shiraz lunged and scrambled up a bank and through a patch of tutu bushes and suddenly we were out on the road. Great relief!

I got off the horse to give him a spell and put my exhausted and footsore dogs around the cattle to bring them back up the road because they'd gone the wrong way. Once we had them mustered we set off up the hill, cattle, dogs, horse and rider, stumbling along with drooping heads.

One of the other blokes had ridden back to look for me and we crossed the slip on the new track they'd dug and joined the rest of the mob without any further misadventures. We'd had enough of those for one day.

We finished the drive with our steers in prime condition and got top prices at the sale for them. I accepted a five-hundred-dollar bonus for retrieving those cattle and shouted Shiraz a flash new cover. I'd cracked a bone in my ankle and it didn't mend right. It gave me a bit of trouble for a while after that.

My horse and I got a reputation over that incident. They called me The Man From Snowy River and Shiraz was asked to sire several foals.

What happened to Shiraz? Well, life took me off in other directions where there was no room for a horse and we had to part. I sold him to some people who ran a horse-trekking outfit and pampered their horses. Shiraz was the hardest animal I ever had to part with.

7

NEVER SEEN
ANYTHING LIKE IT

At the time this happened Henry Buckner and I were running a huntin' and fishin' service for tourists in the Eastern Bay of Plenty. The main part of our operation was a fifteen-foot fibreglass jet-boat with a big Chevy V8 in it, and by jet-boating our clients up the rivers we could practically guarantee them good hunting. It was a very basic operation, the overnight accommodation we provided was a tarpaulin tied across a pole, they slept on the ground and we mainly ate what we caught. The bottom of our jet-boat was more patches than original hull and we could patch it up on the river bank if we needed to when we dinged something, providing it wasn't too serious. Our clients were unanimous in one thing; when they left they all declared that they'd never seen anything like it.

This day we took four German executive types up the Motu River for a day's hunting. The jet-boat was well loaded, with six men and three dogs and quite a bit of gear and the river was lower than we liked it. Some of the shingle bars were going to be marginal, but we decided to play it by ear and set off up the river. We hadn't been going long before we got a big stag on a slip above the river. We dragged it down to the river bank and photographed it and gutted it and hung it in a tree to be picked up on the way back. Just after that the dogs had quite a spectacular scrap with a black boar out on the river stones.

By the time we stopped for lunch we had another deer, four good eating pigs the dogs had caught on the bush flats and two impressive sets of goat horns. Our German clients were in a state of high excitement by this time and were getting stuck into some bottles of square gin they'd brought with them to celebrate their trophies. My mate and I decided that if we could get this lot back down onto the road they'd have had their money's worth. The river was dropping all the time and we were going to have to go for it to get through some of the shallow rocky places.

We got the boat loaded and headed off back down the river. By this time the German executives were well into their second bottle of gin. Manoeuvring the boat down through the rapids at high speed, dodging the rocks and submerged logs, called for some pretty snappy driving, and our German friends thought we were bunging it on just for them.

We made it back to where we'd left the first stag, rather miraculously in a couple of places I thought, and loaded that on as well. We had to tie it onto the bow of the boat as there was no room for it inside. We carried on downriver with six men, two big deer, four pigs, three dogs and gear on the boat – and the worst part of the river was still to come.

Henry was real good at handling the boat and we got away with it for quite a while, avoiding the obstacles and the shallows and watching ahead for that silver V in the water that tells you where the deepest water goes over into the next lot of rapids.

Suddenly we were amongst a scattering of rocks in a seething rapids. We couldn't avoid hitting some of them. We bounced off one rock and slid across another and then rammed into a big one that nearly stopped the boat in its tracks and briefly interrupted the singing our clients had got into. We got through that and out into a stretch of smooth going but we could tell we'd holed the boat. We still had a gorgy part of the river to negotiate and if the boat went down in there we were going to have serious problems. We decided to keep her to the floor and see how far we could get.

By the time we reached the gorgy bit the boat was getting heavy and sluggish and hard to keep up on the plane. The

Germans were waving their bottles around quite unaware how close they were to disaster. The gorge was mean and deep with sheer rock walls and the water swirled and boiled and eddied in the corners. A creepy enough place at the best of times and one of the most dangerous places on the river to end up in the water. It was a worry.

By weaving the boat back and forth to keep it planing we made it through that gorge, and away down the river we caught a glimpse of the road bridge, but by this time we could hear the water lashing around inside the engine cover. It was only a matter of time before she shorted out on us.

"We're not going to make it," said my mate. "We've got to get rid of some of this weight."

I cut the rope holding the stag on the bow and let it go over the side. Then I threw the other deer off the engine cover and the four pigs, all over the side. Then I called the dogs out from under the bow of the boat and threw them over the side as well. If we were going to sink we didn't want them trapped in there. They swam ashore and followed us down the river. It was only about this time that our clients began to twig that we might have some sort of a problem. They stopped singing.

We wallowed down the last stretch of river with the motor missing and surging, and swung her in and rode her straight up onto the shingle on our own bow wave. The motor stopped. There was six inches of water slopping around in the boat. I'll always remember my mate looking at me and saying, "What we've just done is impossible."

I could only nod agreement with him.

Then one of our German clients complained that we didn't tell them we were going to do all that and they'd missed out on getting some good photographs. They carried on toasting their most successful hunting trip.

We backed up the trailer and winched the boat onto it and retrieved our two deer and four pigs when they came floating down across some shallows. There was still water running out of the boat when we dropped our over-excited clients off at their hotel in town.

We had an eighteen-inch split and a round hole punched in the bottom of the boat. We stuck it in the shed and patched the holes with fibreglass and resin and cured it overnight and dried everything out with electric heaters. The next morning, bright and early, we picked our German clients up and took them for a nice quiet day trolling for trout on Lake Matahina.

That day one of the Germans confided to me that yesterday had been a most interesting day indeed. In fact they'd never seen anything like it.

"Nor have we," I assured him.

8

A NEW SHOTGUN

Henry Buckner and I had found this good place for ducks in a little bay over the back of Late Rotoma and on opening day we launched our jet-boat in the dark and swooped over the lake and got to our spot just on daylight.

We were a bit hacked off to discover that someone was there before us. Four blokes in a big flat-nosed punt with an old Seagull outboard motor on it. They must have been there all night. Anyway there were plenty of ducks flying in and we'd got three or four each when the weather suddenly closed in on us. Strong wind and heavy rain. Visibility was suddenly near enough to nothing.

After a while the four blokes in the punt started her up and took off out of the bay. We stuck it out for another half hour or so and it wasn't showing any signs of letting up so we decided to chuck it in for the day.

Out on the lake it was quite rough and we were punching our way through the wind-blown rain and spray when we spotted the punt through the sheets of rain. One of them was standing in the stern pulling on the starter rope. We went over to them. They didn't know what was wrong with their motor, it had just stopped and wouldn't go. We decided we'd have to tow them and they threw us a rope that was attached to a ring in the flat front of the punt.

We pounded slowly across the lake, crouched behind the perspex screen of the jet-boat, jerking in the waves against the dead weight of the punt. We'd been ploughing along like this for about half an hour with the big V8 gurgling along as fast as we dared when I looked around and saw the front of the punt bouncing along on the end of the rope. We'd pulled the end right out of it. I shouted to Henry and he spun the boat round and raced back in the direction we came from.

We found them, and they didn't appreciate how lucky they were. We dragged them one by one into the jet-boat. They all had heavy clothes on and it was only the air trapped in their clothes that had kept them afloat for a while. If we hadn't found them when we did they'd have been goners, but they complained about the loss of their boat and their gear. One of them in particular was grizzling about having lost his new eighteen-hundred-dollar shotgun.

We cruised around and picked up what gear we could find floating, decoys and hats and an oar and – hello, what's this? The cork-line of a tangled four-inch gill net. We lifted it out of the water and here was this bloke's eighteen hundred dollar shotgun. It had fallen through the net and caught at the trigger guard, an absolute fluke. There were also five big rainbow trout still meshed in the net. These blokes had been netting trout, a very serious offence. By this time they were too wet and miserable and cold to care. They threw the net into the bottom of the boat just as it was and left it there.

The bloke was still complaining that his expensive gun had got wet. He was getting on my wick, this joker. Any more complaining and I was going to remind him to count his bloody blessings. Fortunately he subsided into a shivering silence, hunched up against the wind.

It took about an hour to punch our way around to the jetty at the carpark and we'd just tied up when Owen Lacey, the worst possible ranger, appeared out of the rain wanting to check our licences and how many ducks we had. He took one look at the trout in the net and promptly confiscated the boat, our ute and trailer, their car and trailer and the three guns we had left.

It took a couple of hours to sort it all out at the ranger station. The four blokes from the sunken punt explained our part in the drama and took the blame for the netted trout. Finally Owen Lacey told Henry and me we could take our gear and go, and as I reached to take my shotgun from where they were lying on a table the complaining bloke picked up his eighteen-hundred-dollar gun and handed it to me.

"Here's your gun," he said. "You'll need to pull it to bits and dry it out."

I looked at my old shotgun with its sloppy action, taped up stock and bulge in the barrel, not far removed from the muzzle-loader, and then at the brand new one in my hands. Grizzler had lost it anyway and I felt that we'd kind of earned that gun in a way.

"Yeah, thanks," I said, sorry I'd been thinking those things about him being a moaning bastard.

And that's how I came to own a state-of-the-art over-and-under double-barrelled variable-choke Browning shotgun, though I don't seem to be getting any more ducks with it than I did with my old gun. Looks good though!

9

THE MIGHTY MOTU

The Motu River starts away back in the Urewera bush. Still only a stream it runs through cleared hill country for a few miles, a good stretch of water for brown trout. Then, gathering volume from other branches, the Motu plunges into the gorges and ravines of the Raukumara Ranges, a vast area of broken eroding ridges and virgin bush through which it winds its way to the sea. They reckon that some of the creeks in there haven't got Maori names because the Maoris never got in there.

There have been feral goats and pigs in the Motu for as long as anyone can remember, breeding up in large numbers because of the inaccessibility of the habitat. The goats never got across to the eastern side of the river and you could see the difference in the vegetation. In the past few years the red deer and the possum have moved into the Motu bush and flourished on its vegetation. There are also a few wild cattle in there whose ancestors escaped from the settlers.

There's no way anyone could walk the Motu, it's too bluffy. When jet boats became available we found that we could get twenty-odd miles up the river from the road bridge down at the coast, and we took hundreds of pigs and deer and goats out of there, animals that had never been hunted before. The main part of the river remained untouched.

Helicopters came in and revolutionised the whole hunting scene, but in the Motu they were restricted by the fewness of places they could land and the denseness of the bush. In the meantime a few jet-boats, helicopters and lives were lost. You can't muck around with the Motu.

Then came the inflatable river raft. There was a road into the top end of the Motu and we found we could put our raft in and float all the way down to the coast, which took three days. Three days being carried noiselessly through untouched countryside seen by few people. Towering bluffs, cascading waterfalls, slips from top to bottom, and bushflats teaming with pigs, deer, goats and even a wild cattlebeast if you were lucky. It was a wonderful source of good meat.

By the time you arrived out at the road with the dogs exhausted and footsore and the raft laden with meat you were usually rafted-out and it was hard to talk to anyone for a few hours.

This sounds idyllic, but you should never underestimate the Motu. You could see by the piles of twisted, shattered logs thrown up on the bends and the huge boulders rolled around the riverbed that tremendous forces pour down the gorge in the floods.

A mate of mine and I got our own raft and did the Motu many times and had good luck with the weather and the hunting. We always came out with venison and pork, it was like the hunting in the old days. When they were paying good money for feral goats to cross-breed with the Angora we caught and brought out dozens of them. Most of the time we didn't even bother wearing life jackets. We thought we were getting to know the river.

Then on one trip the two of us and our three dogs set off all right and we got four pigs and a deer before it started to rain heavily. We carried on down the river in the rain and camped under our tarp that night in our usual place. It rained all night and we could hear the river coming up. We went out several times with a torch to re-tie the raft, which we had roped to a tree up in the bush.

By daylight it was still raining and the river was up twenty-five feet, starting to float logs and still rising. We weren't rafting in that. The logs were hitting the cliff face on the bend end-on and rearing up into the air and crashing back into the water. We built up our fire and sat round it all day, watching the river come up to thirty-five feet above normal.

It stopped raining that night and we waited all the next day for the river to start going down. The day after that it fell to about twenty feet above normal and no more logs were coming down. We knew that rivers are often easier to raft when they're a bit flooded and decided to give it a go the following morning.

The next day we lashed everything into the raft, put on wetsuits and life jackets, got the dogs to get in and pushed off out into the river. Our meat had gone off so we had to leave it behind. We hadn't gone far before we knew we were in for it. The surge was so powerful that we couldn't control the raft properly. Our paddles were just about useless.

We got carried down a narrow gorge where the waves were ten feet high, and at the end of the gorge the raft slammed into a rock wall and spun off down a set of rapids with one of the dogs swimming alongside. We got the dog back onto the raft and settled down during a comparatively peaceful stretch, but we still had the Slot to negotiate yet and it wasn't far ahead of us. The Slot was a place where the whole river poured through a gap just wide enough to take the raft and then fell twenty feet into a big pool.

Suddenly we were dragged into it, paddling frantically to try and keep the raft straight on. We shot through the gap on the crest of the wave and then fell thirty feet into a seething cauldron of white thrashing water. The back of the raft got sucked into the vortex of the water pouring into the pool and I was wiped off the raft and driven down into the churning current, whirling round and round. I didn't know where the surface was, all I could see were bubbles of air in the water.

I was already a bit breathless from the paddling going into the Slot and just when I was about to start breathing water my foot touched something. I gave a frantic shove and my head popped out of the water about thirty yards downstream from the waterfall. My mate, who'd managed to hang onto the raft, was calling out for me. I managed to yell out as I got swept around a bend and he saw me and paddled after me. I got back onto the raft just before we went down a half mile of jolting, spuming staircase where the river poured down through a jumble of house-sized boulders. One of our dogs was missing and we never saw him again, he must have drowned. My paddle was lost, which made us even less manoeuvrable and we still had one nasty place to negotiate.

This nasty place was where the river drops steeply through some bouldery rapids and then turns sharply along the face of a cliff. Because the river was high we shot down the rapids through a series of big waves and then slammed into the cliff with such force that it doubled the raft in half. We spun off there with the two dogs in the water and only managed to get one of them back on board before we were swept down the next lot of rapids, unable to reach the other dog which was being carried along a few feet away from the raft. We got him about half a mile further downstream.

It went on. The Motu was in a dangerous mood that day. We got the raft wrapped on a boulder in the middle of the river and had to get out on the rock and manhandle it off. Then we eddied-out and went round and round in a backwater, unable to get across the current and out into the main river. We had to climb the bank and drag the raft along the edge with a rope.

Then we got caught in a huge boil in a corner of the river. It came up underneath us and lifted us ten feet and as we slid off the side of it the whole end of the raft got sucked under the water. We nearly turned over and only just popped out the right way up.

By that night we got to a camp site not many miles from the coast. We'd covered two days' distance in a day, and it had been the most hair-raising day's rafting I ever hope to experience. From here on there was nothing to worry us and we got to the road bridge the next day without any major incidents.

That was the only time we ever came out of the Motu without something for the pot, but personally I was grateful to have come out of there at all that time. Teaches a man respect, a thing like that. No one would need to get slotted in the Motu more than the once to learn that one. It doesn't pay to muck around with rivers.

10
CLOSE SHAVES

It sounded romantic, an English journalist had described the Kiwi deer cullers as 'The New Zealand Foreign Legion', but that's about romantic as it ever got. There's not much that's romantic about living and working on your own in the back country. It requires a certain kind of nuttiness and not all of us have it.

Apart from the conditions you have to live in, the diet, the weather and the terrain, there's the loneliness. That'd be the hardest thing to handle. Loneliness has always been all it's cracked up to be. Then there's the fact that you're so distant from any help if you ever get crook or injure yourself. Not everyone's cup of tea, living like that.

I suppose anyone who spends time in the back country has their share of close shaves and maybe your number isn't up until your ticket's been clipped, but nearly all the mishaps I knew of in the bush were because someone had done something stupid, including myself.

In the early days working in the back-country a man was often required to live and work on his own for weeks and even months at a time. This policy was gradually changed until you weren't supposed to stay in the bush for long periods without a mate. We still worked alone every day and it surprises me how few serious incidents there were amongst us.

I've personally been hopelessly bushed a number of times and had to follow some watershed until I came out on a farm or a road of some kind. On one occasion I came out of the bush a hundred miles by road from where I'd entered it.

But it's not only guns and floods and getting lost you have to be careful of in the bush. The most innocent and ordinary things can contribute to a disaster. There were two near-disasters I remember, one of them happened to me and the other to a mate of mine.

The one that happened to me was when I was rabbiting in the central North Island. I was working my way through a block of hilly farm country with sixteen dogs and a shotgun. The burrow-dogs chased a rabbit out of a clump of fern and before I could get a shot at it, or the big dogs could fan out and pick it up, it ducked into a tomo hole about three feet round, like a cave in the bank, and up a rabbit hole a few feet inside the tomo.

The dogs poured in and started digging frantically at the hole and around the edges of the tomo. I got a handful of Cynogas out of the tin in my back-pack and kicked the dogs out of the way and crawled into the tomo to put the granulated cyanide up the rabbit hole and block it up.

I was just reaching forward to toss the cyanide into the rabbit hole when a great blob of earth fell onto me, pinning me to the ground, and the dogs were bringing more down on top of it.

This was a hell of a predicament to be in. It was damp inside the tomo and the Cynogas would already be starting to give off fumes. More dirt thudded down on top of me. It was starting to get dark in there. I opened my hand and let the cyanide spill out onto the damp ground and wiped my hand on the dirt. I was only going to get another couple of breaths before the fumes got to me. I propped my hands on the ground, breathed what could be my last deep breath, and heaved backwards with everything I had in me. I knew that under normal circumstances I could never have shifted such a weight, but these weren't normal circumstances. I burst backwards out of that hole through several hundredweight of loose earth and lay backwards, breathing air. Then I crawled away a few yards and sat there meditating on the various philosophies and religions of the world, while the dogs frolicked around in blissful ignorance of the fact that they'd just bloody near killed me.

The one that happened to this mate of mine was even more far-out than my experience in the tomo hole. It also happened in the central North Island pumice country. We were living and working in the bush and wild pork and venison were a major part of our diet. Doug was an experienced bushman and hunter and this day he'd decided to go out and try to pick up some meat for the pot. He was hunting in a block of native bush that had been logged. You could often pick up something on the old logging tracks.

It had turned into a real dirty day, rain and sleet and wind, as cold as a stepmother's breast. He got a deer, a stag, and gutted it and cut the hocks and locked the front and back legs together and put his arms through and carried it on his back like a pack. He had about an hour's walk out to where he'd left his ute.

The rain got heavier and his hands were numb so he slung his rifle round his neck and stuck his hands in the pockets of his pants and walked along like that. He was going okay until he went to step across a three foot-wide washout in the pumice track and caught the toe of his boot on the end of a stick and it tripped him head-first into the washout.

He was pinned there with the weight of the deer on his back, the rifle was digging into the side of his neck and his arms were wedged so tightly against the side of the washout that he couldn't get his hands out of his pockets. All he could do was wriggle around to try and free himself, but this brought loose pumice down into the washout and there was water running through it from all the rain, and it started coming up to his face. He was gurgling in it by the time he managed to get one arm out and reach his knife and cut the deer off him and dig his way free. Gave him a hell of a fright.

He was a fit, strong man but by the time he got out of that washout Doug was too knackered to carry his deer out. He hung it in a tree and staggered off home. I went out with him the next day to give him a hand to carry the deer in and he showed me where he'd been stuck in the washout. It was just an ordinary washout, the same as thousands of others around there. Funny to think that something so harmless and common could easily have killed a bloke.

It goes to show how easy it is for people on their own in remote places to get into trouble. If someone else had been there neither of those incidents would have been dangerous, they'd have been downright funny, and, as I say, it's quite remarkable that there've been so few fatal accidents in the back country. Or maybe it is a case of your number not being up until your ticket's been clipped. That'd explain it but I don't know if it pays to get too philosophical about a thing like that, just in case it's not right.

11

TOO MUCH OF A
GOOD THING

They reckon you can have too much of a good thing, and if that's right my old mate Stan was a perfect example of it. If anyone ever had too much of the milk of human kindness, Stan did. He had so much of the stuff it affected his judgement and he was always trying to help no-hopers and people who didn't actually need it.

Stan was always a soft touch for anyone with a hard-luck story. After years of being ripped off and let down he wasn't quite so bad as he used to be, but he was always going to be a worry.

When we were young and idealistic he was a downright menace to himself and anyone who happened to be standing near him. There's no doubt that Stan's heart was in the right place, but he was never able to distinguish a lame duck from a dead loss.

I first met Stan when I worked with him for a few months, landscape gardening. We got on well with each other and seeing as he was a bachelor and lived alone in a house I moved into one of his spare rooms. He was okay when we were working, but he liked to go into one of the pubs in town two or three times a week after work and you never knew who or what he was going to bring home with him.

One I'll never forget was a thirty-five-year-old stripper from a nightclub whose boyfriend had kicked her out of the flat. Stan arrived home with her and her bags and they sat up in the early morning hours, drinking Stan's wine and smoking Stan's smokes, working out how they were going to put Daisy back on the road to healthy living and regained self-respect.

I didn't know Stan very well at that stage but it looked to me as though the hard-done-by Daisy was having him on. Personally I wouldn't have left her alone in the house when we went out to work, but Stan reckoned that you have to put your trust in people so that they, in turn, can become trustworthy. I didn't know about that, I went by the old Persian tradition, "Trust in God but tie up your camel".

For the first couple of days Daisy sat around chain-smoking and chain-drinking and making a hell of a mess. It took us half an hour to clean up the kitchen when we got home at night before we could start cooking our dinner. Stan explained that Daisy was going through a process of change and shouldn't have extra demands put on her.

One morning Daisy borrowed a few bucks off Stan so she could go into town and apply for a job as an attendant at the Tepid Baths. Stan drove her to the bus stop and returned jubilant at having inspired such positive action in one of the world's lost souls.

The lost soul arrived home in a taxi in the early hours the following morning and woke the whole street up having an argument out on the footpath with a bloke who finally slammed the door and took off in the taxi. She came in and told us it was her uncle who'd been helping her find work. And still Stan refused to believe she was having him on. Frankly, I was getting heartily sick of cleaning up after this lost soul.

Daisy had two or three temporary relapses into her former ways over the next two or three days. One night she didn't come home at all because there was a suspicious-looking man lurking around outside her girlfriend's flat and she was so scared she had to stay the night there.

Stan actually swallowed all this. I couldn't believe the bloke. By this time Daisy was into him for several hundred dollars for fares, smokes, clothes and a bit of pocket money for self-respect. Several times I tried to point out to Stan that the woman was blatantly bludging off him, but he continued to defend her sincerity, right up until the afternoon he dropped in at home to pick up a compressor we needed on the job and found Daisy naked on his double bed with two naked blokes. Apparently Stan did his block (I'd have liked to have seen that) and kicked them out of the house.

I never saw Daisy again. When I got home that night she was gone, leaving behind her a considerable mess, an empty booze cupboard, a toll bill we had to pay off at so much a month, a staggering overload on our account at the dairy at the corner, and a lacy black high-heeled shoe with a broken buckle.

You'd think an experience like that would have made Stan a bit more selective in the lame duck department, but no, we were still paying the price for his misguided efforts to rehabilitate Daisy when he came home with Al.

Al was a different kettle of fish from Daisy altogether, Stan assured me. Al was a victim of injustice and only needed a helping hand for a while along life's path and he'd be back on top again in no time. Stan liked victims of injustice and could become quite indignant on their behalf.

Stan and Al sat up most of the night and cleaned up a gallon of Old Pale Gold fortified sherry, discussing how they were going to go about getting Al off the booze and started on the road back to the top. We never did find out exactly what Al had been at the top of but we heard plenty about how he'd been toppled.

Al's story was one of treachery and betrayal in business circles, an unfaithful and scheming wife and ungrateful children, the deprivation of a huge inheritance by legal trickery, and unjust ostracism by wealthy and powerful relatives. In despair Al had taken to the drink to try and blot out the pain of it all, but now he was ready to face up to reality and start over again.

As far as I could see Al was a plain alcoholic who was quite happy to tell Stan anything he wanted to hear as long as there was a bit of free booze in it, but there was no way Stan was going to believe me. He didn't want to.

One of the things holding Al back on his pilgrimage back to the top turned out to be that he owed money, two hundred dollars, and being a man of pride he naturally couldn't hold his head up with the shame of debt hanging over him. He confided that he'd also been subjected to threats by the people he owed the money to. As a matter of fact he'd had the money on him up until yesterday, but it had been ripped off by a crooked cop who'd arrested him on false charges of failing to pay fines. When Stan asked him who it was he owed the money to Al replied that it was "er – a bookmaker".

Stan gave Al the two hundred dollars and off Al went in Stan's best white shirt to pay off his debt so he could look the world in the eye again, and with an extra twenty dollars to pick up the meat for dinner on his way home. I had to protest. We were having trouble getting our money for a landscaping job we'd done and we were still paying off what Daisy had cost us, but Stan, bless his oversized heart, said he'd have felt worse if he didn't put a bit of trust in his fellow man.

The only consolation I got out of that one was that I bet Stan twenty bucks we'd never see Al again, and of course we didn't.

But it kept happening. I got up one morning and found a woman sleeping on the couch in the lounge and then discovered two kids in the spare room. She was a refugee from a brutal drunken husband and just needed somewhere to stay until her sister got back from overseas.

She was a disaster. Her kids ran riot round the place, completely out of control, and she whined endlessly about how her terrible husband mistreated her. Stan sat up half the night listening to it.

It wasn't long before I felt like giving her a biff myself. Fortunately she took off before I was driven to doing it. Left a note saying she'd gone back to her husband and thanks for everything, and the crayon scribbles across the lounge wallpaper were all we had left to remind us of her sojourn with us. Stan actually expected her to drop by any day to pay him back the hundred and seventy-five dollars she'd borrowed off him that morning.

I won another twenty bucks off Stan over that, he couldn't believe that anyone could go back to a depraved monster like she'd described her husband to be and I'd bet him she would.

Even that didn't stop him. For a while we had a bloke who'd been persecuted all his life just because of the colour of his skin. No one would employ him or rent him a flat or serve him a beer or give him a bed or lend him a few dollars – just because he was a Maori. A victim of injustice!

Of course Stan had immediately offered him a bed for as long as he liked, and a few dollars to tide him over. Ringi graciously accepted both and responded with a sickening outpouring of phoney flattery and gratitude. Stan was, as usual, completely sucked in and believed Ringi's stories of constant racial persecution from his first day at school right up until Saint Stan had taken him into his heart and restored his faith in humanity. I felt like throwing up.

Ringi accepted Stan's hospitality with the whole-heartedness in which it was offered. He spent the money, ate the food and took over the bed. He went out each day in his tireless search for work, but he always got rejected because of the colour of his skin. It worried Stan no end.

It dragged on for a couple of weeks and then Ringi disappeared. Just went out one day and didn't come back. Then Stan saw in the newspaper where this bloke Ringi-something had been found guilty on several counts of theft. He had a long list of previous convictions and they'd sentenced him to two and a half years in jail. We weren't sure whether it was our Ringi or not at first, then we found a car radio, a video recorder, a hair dryer, an overcoat and a camera, all brand new, under the bed in the room which was once again temporarily spare.

Just to mention another occasion, Stan brought a guy home one night who turned out to be gay. He and Stan had completely misunderstood each other in the pub and I had to get out of bed and intervene to help Stan repel the bloke's advances before things got completely out of control. When I appeared the bloke accused Stan of two-timing him, but he settled down when we explained the situation and accepted a cup of tea and a chocolate chippie with us. That was one of Stan's less expensive rescue operations. They all ended up costing us, but this one only cost us the bloke's taxi fare back into town.

It went on. We were shifting rocks, lugging paving stones around and shovelling soil and building retaining walls and pouring concrete all day, and Stan was giving large hunks of our hard-earned money to all these dead-beats. And he was so downright nice about it that it was hard to stop him.

I was moving on, back to the bush, nothing to do with Stan, and the night before I left he arrived home with a middle-aged country and western singer, complete with guitar and long hair. He looked suspiciously like a drug addict to me, but I left that one to sort itself out, as they all seemed to do in the finish.

I've run into Stan from time to time over the years, and every time I see him or hear news of him he's still at it, propping up the unproppable, unaware of the odds and getting ripped off every time. It's kept him poor. It makes you think that maybe you can have too much of a good thing after all.

12

STREAK'S PUB

One winter a bloke we called Streak and I were doing possums in a block of steep broken bush country, camping in a cold little shack made of opened-up oil drums, two hours' walk in from the road. It rained so much we'd had to give up putting out poison lines and instead ran a hundred traps each. There weren't many possums there, we were lucky to get fifteen good skins a day, but the furs were particularly good and we were averaging fourteen bucks a skin. The money was okay but we sure were earning it.

Hard yakker, that block. We had to cut our trap-lines across the steep watersheds through thick groves of supplejack and kiekie and other thick undergrowth, shifting traps that weren't catching and moving further away from camp every day. We usually got back at night wet, and then it changed to snow and ice and we often had to thaw out the possums by a fire before we could skin them. It was usually ten o'clock at night or so before we'd finished tacking out and scraping the skins.

Streak was okay to live and work with. He was big and powerful and shambling and good-hearted. He was inclined to be a bit slow (that's how he got to be called Streak) and I nearly always got back to camp in the evenings before he did. I also got up before him in the mornings, which meant that I did most of the cooking, but that didn't worry me. Streak's culinary efforts left much to be desired. When you're working as hard as we were you'll usually eat just about anything, but some of the concoctions Streak dished up were downright stomach-churning. Things like rice, onions and possum-legs boiled up together in a revolting mess in a camp oven. Streak couldn't see anything wrong with it but in the circumstances I was only too happy to do all the cooking.

We slogged on through the winter, our only inspiration the money we were making. Then one night we arrived back at the tin hut and found that two mates of ours who were doing helicopter deer-recovery in the next valley had dropped in and left a note for Streak. His aunt had died.

Streak had been orphaned when he was just a shaver and he'd been brought up by this aunt and uncle, who ran a country pub. The uncle had passed on a few years before and now his aunt had followed after him.

Streak wasn't going to make it to the funeral but he decided he ought to go out anyway. He had some gear stashed at this pub and wanted to collect it in case the pub got sold. This meant that I had to go with him because he'd had his driver's licence cancelled the last time we were in town for breathing the wrong kind of breath into a policeman's breath-testing gadget. Besides that we were both ready for a break anyway.

We sprung the traps and packed our skins out to the road and took them to the buyer in town and got nearly fifteen thousand dollars for them. A good skin cheque for those days. In fact it was the best price I ever got for possum furs.

The next day Streak and I drove over to his aunt's pub, then back into town to see a lawyer and then back out to the pub. Streak had inherited the place. We had a pub, an interesting change from the mud and snow and slush and ice we'd been living amongst for the past few weeks.

The two staff had stayed on and kept the pub going. There was a bar-manager called Ned and a Mrs Rankin who did the cooking. We started learning the ropes from them and one of the first ropes we learned was that this Ned was ripping the place off. We'd started keeping track of what was coming in and going out and discovered that notes were going out of the till and bottles of spirits and beer were going out of the stock. What came in was bills, wads of them.

We gave Ned half an hour to get his gear and get the hell out of it. We didn't even pay him and he knew better than to ask. Streak wasn't a bloke who got easily aroused but he would have loved a chance to deal to that Ned for stealing off his aunt.

The bills weren't so easy to get rid of. There was a letter from the brewery informing us that they wouldn't supply any more kegs of beer or spirits until their account was settled. Another from the freight company and another from the electricity supplier said much the same kind of thing, pay up or go out of business.

We decided to pay the accounts off and start from scratch, and by the time we'd done that we'd written out cheques for nine and a half thousand dollars of our possum money.

Within a month we realised that the pub was only just paying its way, and then only if we were real careful not to spend anything that wasn't absolutely necessary. The idea of us taking any wages was out of the question. We even had to pay Mrs Rankin out of our possum money. Then, on top of the rest we discovered that we had a seventy-thousand-dollar mortgage on the pub and the bank wanted the payments brought up to date or 'alternative steps will be taken'. That more than took care of the rest of our possum money. The pub must have been due to go under at the same time as Streak's aunty and we were just propping it up.

Something had to be done. Streak suggested putting the pub on the market, but we couldn't realistically expect people to queue up to buy a pub that was running at a loss. There was only a handful of locals who patronised the place, our main clientele was the passing traffic and that's what it did, it kept passing right on by. We were dependent on the occasional ones who stopped for a drink or a feed. We needed more of them. We decided that we needed something different, something unusual, to attract more customers, and we came up with this hard-case idea.

We spent two hundred and fifty dollars we couldn't afford and got a sign done saying, TUATARA TAVERN. CROOK BEER. DIRTY GLASSES. LOUSY TUCKER. SHORT CHANGE. INCIVILITY. NO TOILETS.

We nailed our new sign on top of the old one and waited to see what sort of effect it would have on our business. The first reaction was that Mrs Rankin packed her bags and left us in indignation at our references to her cooking. I had to do the cooking after that because Streak's cooking was exactly what we'd described on the sign.

Our sign did make people stop, quite a lot of them, but mostly they stopped to photograph our sign and then drove straight on past the pub. A few came in and had a look and some of them even saw a bit of humour in it, but the little bit of custom they brought didn't make any significant difference to our cash-flow problem. It looked like we'd overdone it a bit with the sign.

In fact it was the sign that brought us undone. A little grey bloke in a baggy grey suit pulled up in a little grey car and came into the bar and asked if that was our sign out there. We'd had a few people making snide remarks about our sign and Streak was getting a bit rattled about it.

"Whose bloody sign do you think it is?" he replied.

"Well the incivility you claim on your sign is accurate," said the little grey bloke in the baggy grey suit. "Let's just see how the rest of it stands up shall we?"

The little grey bastard was a health inspector and he went through the place from one end to the other, making a list. He wouldn't accept a beer or even a cup of tea, whereupon Streak told him he was a miserable little bastard, which didn't help our cause much. The little grey bloke in the baggy grey suit left saying we'd be hearing from him, which we sure did. We got a letter from the Health Department saying that unless we immediately upgraded the pub in the following ways our licence to trade would have to be revoked.

We paid a builder to come out and give us the bad news, at

least a hundred and forty thousand dollars to bring the place up to scratch. The building itself needed re-piling, parts of the floor needed replacing and the whole roof would have to be replaced, to mention just a couple of things.

The bloody pub had been sitting there minding its own business for ninety-six years and as soon as we took it over we got landed with all the maintenance that was never done on the place, including a lot of new stuff the little grey bloke in the baggy grey suit had added to it all. He'd ruined us.

Finally we did what any self-respecting bushman does when confronted with little grey bureaucrats in baggy grey suits; we chucked our gear in the ute and headed for the tall timber.

A very expensive spell from the bush, that one. It had cost us more than two thousand dollars a week of our hard-earned possum money. We could have stayed in the flashest pubs and lived like kings for less than that. I never found out what Streak did about that pub in the finish. After the furs started going off he went down to Fiordland, cray-fishing with his cousin, and I did the whitebait season.

I've never seen Streak since. That's how life goes sometimes, but I hope he got something out of that pub of his eventually. We sure earned it.

13

CUTIE-PIE

The thar (pronounced ta) is by far the most agile and sure-footed animal you'll get in the mountains. They're like a big hairy goat to look at and they'll run rings around any goat or chamois. They hang out on the highest, steepest bluffs and they run all over them. It's amazing to see some of the places they can go. If they do fall they can turn round in the air and land on their feet and carry on. They don't have any natural predators in this country and it's often necessary to cull the mobs to keep their numbers down. They completely strip the vegetation if they're left to breed unchecked.

Another bloke and I had been picking off a small mob of thar on a bluff in the head of this valley and we were climbing up some rocks to retrieve the tails when a young bull thar, only a few weeks old, came bouncing around the side and cannoned into me, which was a pretty clumsy thing for a thar to do. I grabbed it and shoved it in my shirt and carted it down to our camp in the valley. And that's how we came by the only pet thar I ever knew.

We called it Thanx and fed it on powdered and condensed milk for about three weeks, during which time Thanx weaned himself onto a diet of bread, rice, porridge, prunes, spuds – just about everything we ate Thanx ate, plus a few extra things like yeast, books, socks, sleeping bag covers and anything else he could reach, and a thar can reach most things. He even ate our last packet of tobacco and got away with it.

Thanx was a hairy little chap with a cute face and a character all of his own. We made him up a bunk in a cardboard box but he preferred to curl up in front of the fire, as close as possible. The hair along his back was always singed from contact with the hot embers. He also had a habit of nibbling at you, probably to see if you were any good to eat. In short, Thanx was a real pet, loaded with mischief, more trouble than he was worth, but a source of constant entertainment around the camp.

We took Thanx with us when we shifted camp because if we'd left him behind he'd have been shot by the next hunters who went up the valley and we didn't like the idea of that, although later on we wished we had. He rode in the cab of the truck with us, perched on top of the back of the seat with his front feet on my shoulder. He liked the truck.

We stopped in a rest area on the coast to stretch our legs and while we were there a tourist bus pulled in and about thirty people got out. At that spot the cliff at the edge of the rest area fell a sheer five hundred feet to where the Tasman rollers crashed into rocks like huge jagged teeth, but it wasn't the spectacular scenery that captured everyone's attention that day.

Thanx was running around and when the bus arrived he hopped up on the top rail of the safety fence around the rest area and stood on a post to get a better look at what was going on. The tourists flipped over him. Photographed him, touched him, called him Cutie-pie, then started feeding him biscuits and stuff, which was what he wanted.

Thanx hopped down off his post to follow a lady he knew had more biscuits in her packet and he was immediately surrounded by tourists, all trying to stroke him at once. He had the kind of hair that made you want to stroke him. Thanx stood on his hind legs and snuffled amongst them to see what there was to eat. They were plainly fascinated by him.

My mate and I were leaning on the fence watching all this and my mate said, "Watch this," and he went over and grabbed Thanx by the scruff and threw him, end over end, out over the cliff.

It had a profound effect on everyone who saw it, that did. It shook me to see Thanx go sailing off over the cliff like that, and I knew there was nothing to worry about. The rest of them went into shock. They were aghast. There was a stunned silence and then some of the women started screaming and crying and the men were trying to calm them down. Their bus driver, red with indignation and outrage, called us a pair of despicable bastards and he was going to report us to the SPCA.

In the midst of all this Thanx himself came bouncing up over the fence and resumed nibbling around for something to eat. There were still some pretty upset people around there when we got Thanx into the truck and took off. We'd done something unforgivable, and yet the one we'd done it to wasn't in the least upset about it. Good fun, as far as Thanx was concerned.

We'd decided to call in at my mate's parents' farm for a couple of days and sort out our gear and repair and make ourselves a few things we needed, and as soon as his mum and sisters spotted Thanx they started cuddling him and calling him Cutie-pie. They begged us to let them keep him there and we'd just assured them that they were more than welcome when Thanx started happening to them.

We were just going inside when he dived past everyone into the house and clattered up the passage, into the lounge, bounced off the arm of the sofa onto the mantelpiece, along the mantelpiece, and onto the top of the bookshelf, scattering photographs and vases and all manner of other expensive bric-a-brac, much of which was now broke-a-brac.

We caught and evicted Thanx with a minimum of further damage and while we were having a cup of tea my mate's mum looked out the window and spotted Thanx standing on his hind legs, stripping her prize sweet peas off the trellis. We caught him again and shut him in the cab of the truck until we could jack up some kind of security.

We weren't successful, partly because of the besotting effect Cutie-pie had on the womenfolk. There wasn't a fence on the place that would keep Thanx in or out but the women wouldn't let us put him in a sheep crate temporarily so we shut him in the woodshed.

We never discovered how Thanx got out of the woodshed but he did, and before he was discovered he'd made one hell of a mess of my mate's mum's years of flower garden, and she still stuck up for him. And there he was on the roof of the woodshed deliberately teasing the working dogs into a frenzy.

My mate's old man had a more realistic attitude towards Thanx, which was hardly surprising. He was a disruptive influence around the place, no matter how bloody cute he was. He was going to have to go before he wrecked the place.

In the finish we had to let the fowls out and shut Thanx in the fowl run. This left twenty-odd chooks to carry on with the wrecking of the garden, but they were nothing compared to the destructive capacity of Cutie-pie Thanx. It was becoming increasingly obvious that Thanx belonged away back amongst the topmost peaks of the Alps, where all there was to break and disrupt was rock.

We were stuck with Thanx. We couldn't release him, we couldn't keep him and we couldn't deal to him. Once you give an animal a name it becomes hard to kill it, but my mate's old man put a time limit on it. If Thanx was still on the place by Friday he was going to blow him away.

It was Thanxsgiving time. Fortunately for him one of the women got in touch with a game-park outfit who were dead keen to have him. They obviously didn't know what pet thars can be like. We dropped Thanx off with them and fled, taking some comfort in the thought that Thanx was going to have a much easier and safer life where he was now than if we'd left him in the mountains, which, it seems, is the best place for them after all.

No more pet thar for me, Thanx.

14

HARRY

I briefly knew this bloke called Harry who things always happened to. You run into blokes like that occasionally. Things just happen to them that don't happen to you and me. The ordinary course of their lives is full of little dramas and it's hard to say how much of it they bring on themselves and how much is accidental. Take the incident of the wheelchair for example.

It was a Saturday afternoon and the bar of the pub we were staying at was filled with a mixture of bushmen, mill workers, helicopter hunters and fishermen, about eighty or a hundred of them. They're normally good-humoured type of blokes but you wouldn't want to get too cheeky amongst them. Hard men.

Harry and I were passing through with eight tourists in a minibus and we were sitting at a couple of tables with jugs of beer. Harry was supposed to be showing me the tour-driving ropes, but all he was demonstrating was how to plough through the day with dramas going on all the time. One of our group was in a wheelchair and he hitched himself across onto one of the pub chairs for a change. Harry sat in the wheelchair to try it out and wheeled it round a bit and then stayed sitting at the table in it.

When we needed another couple of jugs Harry put them in his lap and wheeled over to where they were three deep at the bar. As soon as they saw this bloke in a wheelchair they made a space for him and passed his jugs and money across the bar and one of them carried the jugs back to our table for him.

Harry did this several times. It was a bit of a hoot. Top service! Then the real wheelchair bloke said he wanted to go to the toilet, which was through a door and down a passage from the bar. It was then we realised that if those bushmen at the bar saw Harry standing and walking around they'd probably rip his head off. They don't like having the micky taken out of them, blokes like that.

We had to lift Harry out of the wheelchair and put him in a chair then lift the wheelchair bloke into the wheelchair and I wheeled him out to the toilet. A seventeen-stone fisherman obligingly opened the door for us. When Harry wanted to use the toilet we had to put the wheelchair bloke back in a chair and Harry in the wheelchair and wheel him out to the toilet. The seventeen-stone fisherman looked curiously at us as he opened the door the second time. Something was puzzling him.

We got talking to some of the locals and one of the bushmen asked Harry how he'd ended up in a wheelchair and Harry came up with the yarn about a tree falling on him. Then a bloke Harry knew came in, another tour driver, and of course wanted to know what Harry was doing in a wheelchair. Two meat hunters were sitting with us by this time so Harry had to trot out the yarn about the tree falling on him again. He was going to be explaining that one for a long time to come.

We stayed in the bar all afternoon. We hadn't planned to but we couldn't very well leave. We had two paraplegics and one wheelchair. At one stage Harry accidentally stood up, then he realised that he wasn't supposed to be able to and sat quickly back in the wheelchair, apprehensive in case anyone over at the bar had spotted him.

When the crowd thinned out around dinner time we decided we'd have to make a move. We were booked in for dinner. We sent out a scout who reported that at least half a dozen blokes from the bar were in the dining room and others were coming and going all the time, so we carried out a carefully planned strategy.

We wheeled the wheelchair bloke around the dining room and sat him at a table with the others and then took the wheelchair back to the bar and got Harry. We took them to their rooms and down to breakfast the next morning the same way. It was a blasted nuisance really. Then a quick dash to the bus and we were away from there and the drama of the wheelchair.

One of the things about Harry is that one drama seems to come quickly on the heels of another, and that's how it was. We stopped at a wayside tearooms for lunch and Harry forgot to pay them before we left. A few k's up the road we were overtaken by a police car. They put the siren on us and pulled us up and made us pay the account. Embarrassing!

That evening we arrived at our hotel in Queenstown, where the bus backed over one of the suitcases and Harry got picked on by a drunk moss-picker who came through the lobby when we were booking in and accused Harry of staring at him. There was more drama getting that sorted out. Then at dinner the Aussie waitress spilt a bowl of soup in Harry's lap. Splat!

"Don't worry about it, honey," I told her as she anxiously mopped at Harry with a table napkin. "He attracts soup."

I know all this was actually happening to Harry but I was finding it quite exhausting.

I only did the one trip with Harry. That was enough. The last I heard of him was that he'd got himself and a bunch of tourists accidentally locked in an historic church. They were in there for two and a half hours until someone came along and let them out. The bloke who told me about it reckoned it was a freak accident but I recognised it as a simple case of Harry running true to form.

15

BY THE SEAT OF
OUR PANTS

In the early venison hunting days there were plenty of deer around, the main problem was how to get the meat out to the road once you'd shot it. There were a number of methods; you could carry it out on your back, you could use pack-horses but they were only any use in certain types of country, you could raft the meat down a river on inflatable rafts but they had to be carried in and pumped up and your meat always got wet and wouldn't keep. Some places you could use a tractor or four-wheel-drive at least some of the way. Some of us used jet-boats and hunted from the rivers, which was often quite effective when the conditions were right.

Then helicopters came in and that was the ultimate gadget for venison recovery, but before they started using them we were trying all kinds of methods. It was during this pre-chopper period that my old food-shooting mate, Merv, decided to buy an aeroplane.

Merv and I had been working some of the bush rivers from an under-powered, plywood jet-boat and while we were making a living it was a bit frustrating. We could only get the jet-boat so far up the rivers, and in the heads of those rivers there were thousands of easy deer.

Merv's theory was that if one of us walked into the head of one of the valleys and cleared a landing strip on one of the river beaches the other one could fly the plane in and carry the loads of venison out to the road. It sounded simple enough. The type of aeroplane he was thinking of only needed a hundred yards or so to take off and land in. We'd heard that a bloke down south was making a packet using the same kind of plane.

So Merv took off to the big smoke, where he stayed with his sister and brother-in-law while he went through a flying course. He arrived back two months later with ten hours' solo flying time in his log book. He'd heard of a plane a farmer in Otago had for sale. It sounded like just what we needed, so we drove over there to have a look at it.

We found the place. It was an untidy, run-down sheep farm with machinery and old truck and tractor bodies scattered around. The plane was parked in a falling-down shed inside the front gate. It was a yellow Piper Cub.

The bloke came out and we got talking and came to the conclusion that we could just afford it if we sold the jet-boat and a section Merv had in Greymouth. The paperwork seemed to pan out okay, the only thing left to do was take the plane for a spin, only there was no airstrip anywhere around.

That was no trouble. The bloke got me to stand on a rise near the front gate and signal to him if anything was coming up the road. He and Merv got into the plane and fired it up and taxied out the gate and gunned it down the metalled road and took off up between the power and telephone wires.

They stooged around in the sky for a while and then made sure there was no traffic coming and Merv landed the plane on the road outside the gate and taxied it up to the shed. I was impressed. Those Piper Cubs sure could take off and land in a short distance. Merv was pleased with it and three weeks later we had it sitting on a swampy airstrip on the West Coast. We took the back seat out and replaced it with a stainless-steel tray that filled the space behind the pilot's seat for carrying loads of meat.

I spent two days walking in to the headwaters of one of the rivers, where I found a fairly level river beach and cleared all the larger stones off a hundred-and-fifty-yard stretch of it and marked out the strip with a spray-can of orange paint. There were deer standing around on slips and ridges watching me as I worked.

When I'd finished making the landing strip I shot six deer and gutted them and dragged them down and hung them in some trees near the strip. Merv flew up the valley and landed without any trouble and in three trips we had the six deer and me down at the road. Two days' walking had become ten minutes' flying.

One of the advantages of having a plane was that we could go where we weren't supposed to and we had our pick of some great hunting country. We were making good money and getting good at our operation. Then, typical young blokes, we started getting cheeky with the weather, never a good idea in the mountains.

It started with small things, like going in for one more load and having to land in the dark. Quite often we'd buzz our mate's house and he'd send one of the kids down to turn the headlights of our ute on, which we always parked at the end of the landing strip. A few times we flew into places and risked landing on smooth-looking spots without walking in and preparing them. That was a bit hair-raising at times.

Once we landed on a strip of shingle at the foot of a glacier, high up in a river valley. We'd shot three deer and dragged them down to the plane before we realised that we weren't going to be able to take off. The slope of the shingle and the direction of the wind didn't equate with a lift-off. We had to cut down two big trees that were in our flight path with a blunt axe. We left our deer behind, got in and gunned her across the shingle and lifted off and banked away from the bush-face almost stalling and got out of there by the skin of our teeth.

The thing that really woke me up to how dangerously we were living, though, was one day when we were flying venison out of a bushed valley. Merv had taken a load out and I was waiting with a stag for our last load. We'd noticed the weather closing in a bit but had decided to risk it, and while he was away a bank of cloud closed in over the valley. Merv dropped in out of the mist and we loaded up and took off, with me sitting in the back on top of the stag.

We flew up into cloud, it started raining and blowing. Suddenly we were whited-out, completely blinded, and the plane was lifting and dropping and ducking around in the gale. We kept climbing and going straight down the valley using the compass. Valleys bend and compasses don't, we could only keep gaining what height we could and hope to clear the ridges or the cloud.

After about twenty minutes of this the wind dropped away but the rain and mist still cut our visibility to nearly nothing. We figured we must be out over the sea by this time so we began to cautiously lose height until we could glimpse the waves down through the mist. Then we turned and flew back towards the coast. Visibility was fifty to a hundred yards by this time and we had to swerve violently away when the bush at the head of the beach suddenly stood in front of us.

We followed the beach. A rocky cliff slid by under one wing a few feet away. We were low on gas, we hadn't allowed for this. By this time I was convinced we were going to have to crash land. It was going to be impossible to find the airstrip in these conditions.

Suddenly we had to bank away from a big clump of old pine trees.

"I know where we are!" shouted Merv. "Andy Norton's place is just over here. We can land in his paddock, I've done it before."

We circled over and found Andy's house and did a low run across his paddock to chase the horses and cattle out of the way, and then we landed. I got out of the plane shaking. We'd gone through all that for a stag worth about two hundred dollars. If I had any flying in my blood it had all been used up in that one flight.

We were more respectful of the weather after that, but our flying days were numbered anyway. The choppers came into the district, there were four of them stationed at our airstrip. There was no way we could compete with them, they creamed off all the easy deer. Wherever we went they'd been there and there was nothing left for us. We were obsolete, but it had been fun while it lasted and we'd done all right out of it, and we were still both alive.

We sold the plane to a bloke who used it for years, carting whitebait from the trenches at the river mouths out to the depot. Merv got a job shooting for one of the choppers and I went seeking adventure hunting crocodiles in the swamps of North Queensland.

Merv ended up flying a chopper of his own, survived many years of it and then retired from it, but I still prefer to be able to get out and walk if something goes wrong.

16

NOT CUT OUT FOR IT

There's no getting away from it, some of us are cut out for certain types of activity and others are not. How many times have you heard someone say, "He's just not cut out for it." And that's usually the stone end of it, the final pronouncement. The bloke's just no good at it and never likely to come right.

Well, I'm not cut out for painting, never was any good at it. Over the years I've had a go at painting things a few times and it always ends up the same, paint all over everything around and someone else usually has to go over the job and tidy it up.

One of my more memorable disasters was painting the roof of a Rabbit Board house in the Wairarapa. It was coming up to Christmas and most of the people who worked on the Rabbit Board wanted to go away on holiday. I didn't have anywhere particular I wanted to go so I volunteered to stay on and feed everyone's dogs and do a bit of maintenance work and some handy rabbiting – on full pay.

Before he left for three weeks' holiday at a bach he had the use of up the Coromandel, the Rabbit Board inspector told me he wanted the roof of one of the Rabbit Board houses painted. There were four tins of paint and some brushes and stuff in the shed there. If I needed any more paint I could book it up at the hardware store in town. I didn't bother explaining how I wasn't cut out for painting, told him I'd try and get round to it and it was left at that.

The only other rabbiter who was staying on over Christmas,

my off-sider, was a gentleman who rejoiced in the name of Aussie Pete, who'd just joined us a couple of weeks before. He was a decent enough bloke, Pete, but he was terribly, painfully, teeth-grittingly slow. There were times I could have sworn he'd gone to sleep standing up.

We'd go out with shotguns and dogs to work a block of country and I'd position Aussie Pete in the right place and then put the dogs through a patch of scrub and rabbits would run all round him. By the time he'd decided which one to shoot at and got his safety catch off the rabbits would be gone. I'd get twenty or thirty rabbits for the day and Aussie Pete would have fired two shots into the ground. He was as much menace to the dogs as he was to the rabbits. Not cut out for it at all.

One day I sent Aussie Pete the other way round a block of scrub and told him I'd meet him by the creek at the other end. He wasn't there when I arrived and I found him some distance down the creek lying spread-eagled in the sun. He'd lain down in the shade of a tree for a rest and the shadow had shifted off him and he'd been lying face up in the sun for two hours. His eyelids, lips and cheeks were badly burned and he was getting headaches so I took him in to the doctor, who sent him to hospital in an ambulance.

Aussie Pete spent his Christmas in the hospital and when he came back to work he hadn't improved. He was as slow as ever. When he got out to open a gate you felt like turning the motor off to save gas, he was that slow.

After Christmas there was a spell of hot weather. The prospect of rabbiting with Aussie Pete wasn't all that attractive so I decided to have a go at this roof the boss wanted painted. I asked Aussie Pete if he'd ever had anything to do with painting and, sure, he and his brother used to go round painting woolsheds on contract. Had two other blokes working for them at one stage.

This sounded all right to me. I'd never tackled a painting job of this magnitude before, but with Aussie Pete's experience I couldn't see how we could go wrong. After all it was simply a matter of painting the stuff onto the roof. We went out to the house and got a tin of green paint each, oil-based green paint, and levered the lids off and stirred the paint with sticks. Then we got a brush each and climbed up the ladder and started painting the roof from the top down.

It was slow work and to speed things up a bit I started pouring the paint onto the corrugated iron and then brushed it out, to save having to dip the brush into the tin all the time. This soon put me ahead of Aussie Pete and I showed him how to do it, but he was so slow that the paint kept getting past him and running down the corrugations towards the guttering. I had to keep an eye on him and go to his assistance a few times.

We ran out of paint before we'd finished one side of the roof, but by the time we knocked off we'd developed a system of really getting the paint on. We found a yard broom and a house broom and we'd pour the paint across the corrugated iron and brush it even with the brooms. Saved all that tedious hand-brushing. Another day and we should have the job finished.

The next day we picked up five more tins of paint and I dropped Aussie Pete off to carry on with the roof while I went off to exercise and feed some packs of dogs we were looking after for the other rabbiters.

It was mid-afternoon by the time I got back to the big painting job. There was a small patch of roof Aussie Pete had painted but no sign of him. I found him in the kitchen of the house trying to wash green paint off his clothes. He'd had a slight accident and was in a fair old mess. We decided to carry on and got stuck into it, and by the time we ran out of paint again we only had a few feet to finish off at one end of the roof. The next day we picked up two more gallons of paint and went out to finish the job.

From the road the new paint job looked a bit streaky, but it was definitely green. Probably going to need a bit of touching up here and there. Then when we got up on the roof we discovered a disturbing thing. The paint we'd applied so lavishly the day before had run down the hot iron into the guttering, and along the guttering into the water tank. Hardly any of it had stuck to the roof at all. It looked like most of the paint had gone into the tank.

We finished painting the roof and had to walk through wet paint to get to the ladder. With the last of the paint we went over some bare-looking patches. Then we unbolted the pipe to the house and let the 400-gallon tank drain out onto the ground. Then we started scraping all the thick green paint, mixed with leaves and dirt and dead birds out of the guttering. We were plastered with the stuff by the time we'd finished.

The green paint had settled in a layer on the bottom of the water tank, and now there was no water left to wash it out with. We tried scraping it, sweeping it, newspaper, Aussie Pete's shirt – and all we were doing was spreading it around. In the finish we rolled the tank down off the stand and poured a couple of gallons of petrol into it and sloshed it around and then let the green petrol drain out, killing a large patch of the lawn in the process.

We did this twice more and got rid of most of the paint, though there was still a green film of it around most of the inside of the tank, which now also stank of petrol. We decided to leave it overnight to air and went home.

The next day we had another look at the tank and then rolled it over against the end of the shed and threw some firewood into it. Then we went into town and ordered a new tank.

I was glad Aussie Pete was there to take some of the blame for the mess we'd left the Rabbit Board's house in. When he arrived back from his holiday and saw what we'd done the Rabbit Board inspector was quite angry, and you couldn't blame him really. There was green paint all over the place. On the walls, the door handles, all over the concrete paths, the windows - everything we'd touched had green paint on it, and yet the roof, where we'd originally put the stuff, had remarkably little on it. You could still see the rust patches from the road.

"Eleven gallons of paint!" said the Rabbit Board Inspector, waving the account from the hardware store at us. "How the hell could you use eleven gallons of paint on a roof that size? You could have painted three roofs!"

And on top of that there was the new water tank to explain. We only just kept our jobs over that painting job, though Aussie Pete lost his soon after. He wasn't cut out for rabbiting. And to this day I still don't know how they get the paint to stick onto roofs, and I'm not even curious about it. I'm just not cut out for painting.

17

NOT CRICKET

One winter I was put on ranger duties, patrolling some of the rivers running into Lake Taupo for trout-poachers, who were inclined to help themselves too blatantly if they weren't watched. It wasn't a job I was all that ardent about but it was all they had for me at the time and it was possible to fit a bit of pig hunting in with it. I only had to warn anyone I caught poaching unless they got too cheeky, and I had the area to myself so it wasn't such a bad job.

I was living in a hut near the mouth of one of the most famous trout rivers in the world and I didn't mind a bit of trout fishing. If I wanted a trout I used to put a cricket on a wet fly and let it down into the pool outside my hut, where there were always trout lying. Never missed. My rod was an old tank aerial and my reel was a cheap worn-out thing with either full drag or none at all. Landing a trout with that gear was a bit of an art but I got my share of them.

In Taupo there lived a retired headmaster of a high-class public school in England. He was a stickler for doing the right thing. I'll call him Noel. Noel was a fanatical trout-fisherperson. He'd retired to Taupo for the trout fishing. He'd written a book about fly-fishing. He invented and tied his own trout-flies. He hosted other eminent trout-fisherpersons from around the world on trout-fishing safaris. They thrashed the mouth of the river, rows of them in chest-waders, each casting the fly of his choice out into the trout-rich rip at the river mouth. They also fished the pools upstream, and they usually caught trout.

I got on okay with the good headmaster. We saw a bit of each other around the lake and the rivers. He winced a bit at some of my attitudes but we were on what you might call cordial terms. He autographed one of his books for me and gave me some of his trout flies.

Three or four times Noel and his mates had been fishing the river mouth when I'd wandered over to the pool by my hut and dropped a cricket into it and immediately hooked out a nice fat trout and wandered back to the hut with it. I could tell that it had Noel intrigued. Several times when we were talking I could tell he was trying to find out what sort of fly I was using to catch those trout with. Finally one day he asked me straight-out.

"Crickets," I told him.

The headmaster laughed. To him the idea of a ranger using illegal live bait to catch trout was so preposterous it was beyond belief. He assumed I just wasn't telling him, and that made him more curious than ever. A couple of times I went out and caught a trout when he was fishing there, just to tease him. And it never failed, every time I dropped a cricket into the pool I immediately got a strike. The trout couldn't resist them, and Noel got more curious.

I joined Noel and two of his German clients on a fly-fishing trip up the Tongariro River one day. They were all expert fly-fishermen and had fished trout rivers all over the world. I had a tattered old wet fly on my trace, a fly that Noel himself had invented. I walked a few pools upstream beyond the rest of them and got a matchboxful of huhu grubs out of a rotten log along the way.

I put a huhu grub on my hook and let it down into the pool and immediately got a good strike. That one got off but I caught two five-pounders in the next pool I tried and within an hour I had four trout, averaging about five pounds' weight. Enough for anyone. I rejoined the others (who'd caught three trout between them), still with the same tattered old fly on my trace.

I knew that Noel knew I wasn't catching those trout on that

fly, even though it was one of his own inventions. He asked me again what I was actually using.

"Huhu grubs," I told him.

He couldn't believe it. Rangers just didn't do that sort of thing. If I'd told him I didn't have a fishing licence he probably wouldn't have believed that either, but I didn't.

One morning I was just getting ready to go out on a patrol when Noel drove up with three blokes in his station wagon. He got me aside and told me he was somewhat embarrassed. He'd guaranteed these clients that they'd catch trout, and the trout had gone right off. They'd fished all the day before and hadn't got so much as a touch. Could I suggest anything?

"Sure," I said. "All you have to do is tie on a wet fly with hardly any feather left on it. Then you get a cricket from under a dry cow pat, stick it on your hook and let it down into the pool. You'll catch 'em that way. If anyone comes along, rangers or anyone like that, you just have to give your line a rip and tear the cricket off your hook and you're all legal again."

The headmaster was outraged at the suggestion. He could never countenance such a thing. If he ever had to stoop to anything like that to catch a trout he would never wet another line. If he ever saw anyone doing anything like that he'd have no hesitation in reporting them to the ranger. He marched off as though he was on parade and I began to wonder if I hadn't taken the headmaster into my confidence a bit more than was discreet.

As I drove off on my patrol I saw Noel and his clients walking up the riverbank with their trout rods and creels. That afternoon I arrived back at the river mouth at the same time as they did and, kia ora! They'd got themselves a good mess of fish. Six nice rainbows!

Now I'm not saying anything. I'm only a humble bushman. It's not for someone like me to suggest anything about the integrity of retired headmasters of high-class public schools in England. Who am I to imagine that a man from the very pinnacle of the pastime, a man globally recognised as a fly-fishing purist with an impeccable reputation, a man with whom us rangers ourselves had been asked to co-operate – who am I to imagine that such a man would do what I think he might have done that day?

My reasons for thinking those almost-blasphemous things were quite circumstantial really, but when you take a cricket from under a dry cow pat to catch a trout with you always put the cow pat back the way it was. The fact that half the dry cow pats in the paddock up the river where Noel and his clients went fishing that day were left turned over might just have been coincidence. No, he wouldn't do a thing like that, would he?

It wouldn't be cricket.

18
BOOTS

In the back country there's one piece of equipment that's more important than your rifle, your pack, your clothing or your sleeping bag, and that's your boots. Not too many years ago there was only one type of boot you could get that was suitable to wear in the bush. Thick bullock hide, hobnails, metal toe and heel plates and leather laces. By the time you had a pair broken in they were half worn out and your feet always had to compromise to fit the boots. You had to soak them in leather dressing or wear them wet until you could walk in them all day without ending up crippled.

Leather boot laces were never very reliable. Fishing cord was often used as a more dependable lace and when braided nylon arrived on the scene it was the best of all. I've seen it so cold in the mountains that if you took your boots off wet they'd freeze solid during the night and the leather laces would snap when you tried to tie them.

Some of us used to pull the toeplates off our boots and put a row of tricounis, or even horseshoe nails, around the edge of the sole, especially if we were working in rocky country. They were noisy to hunt in but your boots lasted a bit longer than they normally would have and gave you a better grip. Then they brought out a rubber-soled boot that wore better in some conditions, especially around river boulders, but the boot itself was still thick and unyielding.

In later years we found that the short, rubberised, lace-up gumboot was lighter and more comfortable than the leather ones, especially if you bought them a couple of sizes larger than you needed and wore two pairs of socks in them. If we were working in creeks and rivers all the time we'd sometimes burn a couple of holes in the instep just above the sole with a hot wire, so we weren't carrying bootfuls of water all the time.

There are many yarns about boots. One I remember concerned one of the compo-kings who used to go from job to job, injuring themselves so they could go on compo. Having got the money they usually boozed it up and when they were broke they'd get another job and do the same thing again somewhere else.

This bloke was working in the native bush, clearing around trees that were to be felled for timber. On his second day on the job he hobbled out of the bush with his shirtsleeve wrapped around a badly gashed foot. Reckoned his axe had slid off a tree root and into his foot. The funny thing about it was that one of the blokes found his boot out in the bush a few days later, without a mark on it.

When I was a young bloke hunting on a deer block in the Kaimanawa Ranges one season, there was a shortage of shooters so I had to live and work on my own, which suited me okay. I had the block to myself and I was going for the top tally that year, away before daylight and back to the hut after dark. We were taking the skins that season and it was hard yakker to build up a decent tally.

About a third of the way through the season my field officer arrived in with two pack horses of supplies, which I was very pleased to see. He told me that I was to train two new shooters he was putting on the next block, which I wasn't pleased to hear. The Field Officer took my dried skins out on the horses and after a couple of days I stuffed my sleeping bag and a bit of ammunition into my pack and set off on the seven-hour walk to a sheep station where we had the use of a hut for a base camp.

The two new shooters were there when I arrived. I showed them how to bake bread in a camp oven and other things they needed to know about camp duties, and checked them on rifle handling and safety. They weren't that good. The following day we each loaded about a hundred and fifty pounds of gear and supplies into our packs and set off on the five-hour walk up a creek to a tent-camp we'd put up on their block the previous season. That block was lower down on the mountains than mine and was mostly rivers and bush with a few clearings here and there.

By this time I could see that neither of these blokes was likely to last the season out, so it was all rather a waste of time. My time. There were deer running around on the tops waiting to be shot and here I was running around down in the bush.

I'd been hunting mostly in tussock and snowgrass country and that does things to your boots. As you walk along the tussock whips across the top of your boot-sole and drags down the front of the upper. After a few weeks of this it wears a neat slit through the front of the boot. This could be quite serious because it's all pumice country around there and if you get bits of pumice in your boot it'll cut your socks and feet and it could easily cripple you if you don't stop and get it out.

As we walked up the creek that day, crossing and re-crossing the stream from flat to flat, the water in my boots was squirting out the slits in the front of them, which made them lighter to walk in and less noisy, no squelching.

"That's a good idea, having slits in your boots like that," said one of the new shooters. "It lets all the water out!"

I just grunted in reply. I'd already taught these blokes more than they were going to use.

We got four deer on the way to their camp and I showed them how to skin them and loaded the skins on top of their packs. We should have got at least twice as many but they were both lousy shots.

By the time we reached the camp it was dark and both the new shooters were complaining about blisters and cramps and aching backs and shoulders. The next morning I left the new blokes in their sleeping bags and nicked out for a daylight shoot upstream from the camp. I got back about mid-morning with four more skins. They hadn't been up long and hadn't even lit the fire yet, but they had cut big slits in the front of their new boots to let the water out when they walked in the creek, which, in that country, was tantamount to crippling themselves.

I didn't say anything about it and left them there to carry on as best they could. A few weeks later when the field officer came in with more supplies he informed me that the new shooters on the next block had lasted less than two weeks and all they'd left behind them was a note in the base camp saying that their feet had packed up and they'd had to leave the job.

Nowadays when I go into the bush I wear Nike or Reebok sport shoes and watch where I put my feet. Much more comfortable.

19

STATE HIGHWAY SIX

For my money State Highway Six has got more going for it than any other road in New Zealand. From the Marlborough Plains, down through the jungles and bluffs of the Buller Gorge to the fantastic coastline of Punakaiki, down through Greymouth, then Hokitika, down the coast to the glaciers and the lakes, the bush, the rivers and the Alps, cross the wide Haast river and follow its winding corridor through the bush and up over the waterfalls and cliffs of the Haast Pass to the lakes and tussock of sprawling Otago and right across the South Island to Invercargill.

The characters who live along State Highway Six are as varied and colourful as the countryside they inhabit. Miners and bushmen, fishermen and farmers, they'll turn their hand to anything. Battlers, good-hearted, great sense of humour. We had many good times with our friends along State Highway Six.

One of my favourite parts of this most interesting road is the South Westland area. They're a bit of a strange bunch, the Coasters. They take their time over things and it doesn't pay to start getting impatient with them. My first introduction to the South Westland character was in the early sixties. I'd bought a big lumbering World War II Morris gun tractor to use for meat-hunting in the South Westland river-beds.

I trundled into Bruce Bay. The road wasn't through to Haast and ended just down past Bruce Bay which was the last outpost, a house, a shop, a shed and a petrol pump. It was more than a hundred miles of metalled, pot-holed road back to the last place you could get any supplies or gas. The shop, which was also the post office, was open but there was no one around. It was getting on in the day and I wanted to get as far up the Paringa River as I could before dark and I needed gas and supplies. I climbed up into my gun tractor to sit and wait. Then I spotted someone, a bloke, mucking around with something out on the river-bed down towards the sea.

After a while I decided to drive out there and find out if he knew where the shop people were. I put her in four-wheel drive and drove down a bank off the road and across a small branch of the river and over the bouldery riverbed right up to where this old bloke was shovelling gravel to set his whitebait net in the edge of the river. Right up to him in a dirty big gun tractor, and he didn't even look up from what he was doing.

"Gidday," I said. "Do you know who's supposed to be looking after the store over there?"

"I am," he said.

"I need some gas and supplies," I said. "I want to get up to Paringa tonight if I can."

"I'll be over there later on," he said, looking up for the first time.

Then he resumed his shovelling and I drove back over to the store and waited for him. Just on dark he shouldered his gear and wandered over to the store and put his net and shovel and bucket in the shed. By this time I was out of my gun tractor, which was parked thirstily beside his petrol pump.

"You wanted a bit of stuff from the shop," he said.

By the time I'd stocked up and gassed up it was dark.

"Where'd you say you were going?" the old bloke said.

"Up the Paringa," I said.

"Well you've left it too late to get up there tonight," he said. "You'd better come over to the house and have a beer. The missus'll be home from town any time. She can slap a feed on."

I stayed the night with them. Beer, fresh whitebait, salad and bread. A great couple, couldn't do enough for you. We became good friends and stayed that way for many years.

I'd learnt my first lesson about the inhabitants of this part of State Highway Six. They're very generous and hospitable but you should never try to interrupt a Coaster when they're whitebaiting. It doesn't get you anywhere.

Years later my wife and I cruised up and down SH 6 in our Model A truck, sleeping in the back and living off the land. We'd stop at a rest area and when the last of the tourists had gone we'd set two or three possum traps around the area and bait them with plain flour.

Possums are nosey beggars and we found that there were more of them around the rest areas than any other spot. We got some good skins off them too. When we heard a possum get caught in a trap one of us would get up, grab the torch, deal to the possum and hang it in a tree and re-set the trap. It wasn't unusual for us to get three or four good skins in a night that way and we could go around the different rest areas again and again.

In the mornings we'd skin the possums we'd caught in the night and put the skins on boards, which we bungied on the front of the Model A to dry as we drove along. That night, in another rest area, we'd take the dried skins off the boards and scrape them and brush them, add them to the bundle in the box and then set our traps, stapling them to the tables and seats around the rest area. At an average of six dollars a skin from the buyer in Hokitika we were making enough to live on. If we had an extra expense, like having to buy a tyre or a battery or something, we'd camp somewhere for a while and run serious trap lines until we had enough money for what we wanted.

During the day we'd fish for a trout or hunt for a deer or prospect for gold or search for greenstone. Our collection of interesting rocks and stones and driftwood was totally out of proportion to the way we were fixed for living space.

As the whitebait season approached there was always a bit of excitement and preparation. Almost to a man everyone working on the road took sick leave. In plenty of time we had our camp and our stand set up in one of the river mouths near the sea. A little village would spring up along the banks of the river, every stand sticking out into the river like a row of rickety jetties.

As well as the locals the whitebaiters were a very mixed bunch, many of them came back to the same place year after year. There were a few retired couples and a sprinkling of loners. There were farmers and mechanics and shopkeepers, builders, busdrivers, bushmen, doctors – anyone you ran into could be anyone from anywhere. All brought together by a mutual fascination with whitebaiting.

There can be good money in whitebaiting if you get a good run of them. We did so well one year we had enough money to pay cash for a brand-new motor bike, and didn't we groove up and down State Highway Six on that thing! We often used it for dragging bundles of firewood down the road to where we were camped.

Great memories of SH6. Sleeping out on the beach with the Tasman rollers crashing onto the rocks a few yards away from the truck. Sitting up to our necks in some hot pools we knew of, surrounded by towering rock faces with snow and ice on everything except us. Hunkered around a fire at the foot of a glacier with the keas putting on a performance for us. Standing in a wide riverbed with the rain splashing into our mugs of tea which we'd made with a fire under a log, so soaked we couldn't get any wetter but still able to have a hot brew. Lugging a forty-pound lump of greenstone for an hour and a half down a gorge and then another seventeen miles balancing it on the bike, only to be told that it was valueless serpentine. Looked like greenstone to us.

Feasts of crayfish, paua, mussels, cockles and bread out on the beach among the driftwood with a fire that lit up the night. At another time matured venison back-steaks barbecued on the old mill-blade we kept snookered at one of our favourite camping places. Fresh salmon and watercress steamed in the embers on the shores of a lake. Great feeds, great times!

That's not to mention the freezing wind and rain and sleet and ice and snow and mud of a winter in Rough Creek. The sandflies and the endless days and nights of rain, the almost continuous flooding of the river, cutting you off from your possum lines. Never completely dry or properly warm until you wonder what the hell you're doing here. Then it clears up and you get a spell of weather so clear and fine you feel as though you could almost reach out and touch the Alps, glistering with new snow like some kind of magnified confectionery.

That's when you spread everything out on the bushes to steam dry in the warm sun, light the fire under the drum and soak in a hot bath for a while, peel enough spuds for a full camp oven of hash and hang it over the open fire, pour yourself another mug of tea, throw something at the weka, lean back against your favourite log and soak up the atmosphere. Wouldn't be dead for quids!

20

A LOT
OF BULL

I was trapping furs and hunting venison on a run-down sheep and cattle station when this lot happened. Most of the country there was steep, eroded and growing back into fern and scrub and second-generation native bush. It hadn't been farmed for years when this young couple took it over. Betty and Gavin, a good keen couple.

They worked from daylight to dark and then some. I'd come down off my possum line and find Gavin optimistically dragging a stretch of rusted wire and rotten posts out of the fern and patching up a fence, while Betty toiled up the hill with a couple of posts on her shoulder, in pouring rain. They rebuilt the access tracks with a little old D2 bulldozer they had and put some of the culverts and bridges back where they belonged, where they could.

Gavin was handy with the hammer and saw and was doing some resurrection on the old house and buildings whenever he had a spare hour or two, but there's a limit to what you can do with rotten timber, rusty iron and no money. Betty did her best in the old house, but the pilings were rotted away and the floors sagged to the point where it was unsafe to walk in some places and they were marked out or blocked off with bits of furniture and, in one place on the veranda, stones from the river crossing.

I helped them whenever I could but there was so much that needed doing I couldn't help feeling it was a bit of a lost cause. Their optimism kept all three of us going. From high on the ridges I could hear Gavin and Betty banging and bulldozing down in the valley. They talked about having the place (the station) ready to put stock on pretty soon now.

I was away selling my possum skins when Gavin got killed. He didn't have a chance. A section of a track gave way under his tractor and sent him plunging three hundred feet down the slope into the river. At the funeral I asked Betty what she was going to do now and she said simply that she was going to carry on, stock the station and farm it, of course.

The idea was preposterous. No one believed that Gavin and Betty could have ever made a living off the place. Now, with Gavin gone, Betty was even less likely to be able to make a go of it. But she persisted and everyone did their best to help her.

She consulted the farm adviser at the Stock and Station Agents to the area and after a bit of research they came up with her best option. Bulls. They were fetching good prices at the works and if she could raise a hundred bulls on the place it could be economically viable. The stock company agreed to advance her five thousand dollars worth of stock food. Local stock breeders donated (or sold her at mate's rates) all the bull calves they could spare. I was recruited to drive all over the district with a borrowed trailer, collecting all these calves and taking them to her place, where Betty took each one under her wing and started hand-feeding them on milk mixed up from powder. With some extra donations she ended up with a hundred and thirty-five bull calves of many different breeds and colours.

My last job before leaving there for the summer was to fix up the fence around the house to save Betty getting mobbed by the hundred and thirty-five bull calves clambering for more milk. The whole place was filled with the sound of blaring calves, but she'd done it so far, with a little help from her friends. She had her farm stocked with a herd of bull calves.

One of the things about bull calves is that they grow up into bulls, and when I returned the following year to do my trap lines again I was treated to an unforgettable sight. Betty was about to give her bulls their daily feed of hay and nuts, which was a matter of going out onto the one flat area beyond the house and calling them.

"Come on boys! Come on!" she called out. And a bellowing multi-coloured rabble of bulls came pouring down the hillsides out of the fern and scrub from all directions and lined up scoffing at the rows of hay and nuts we'd spread out. I was impressed. A hundred and thirty-five bulls in one mob is an awe-inspiring sight at any time but Betty walked amongst them as though they were lambs, slapping their rumps and shoving and ordering them around.

Betty's bulls were looking good. She'd had some help with getting her yards fixed up and the bulls drenched, and they must have been getting enough tucker among the scrub and off the patches of grass left in the valley. She'd done it, and mostly alone, turning down two offers of marriage in the meantime.

As winter closed in on the valley it became obvious that the bulls would have to go. There just wasn't enough grass or money to keep them fed and they were beginning to lose condition. Two stock agents came out and looked them over and gave Betty their verdict, sell them by auction on the place. When prospective buyers saw the country they came off they'd realise how easy it would be to fatten them up for the works on a bit of decent grass.

On the day of the sale it was raining. The fifty or so buyers lined up in their oilskins and hats behind the fence. I overheard some of them complaining about the stock not having been yarded for inspection. Then Betty called the bulls and they came pouring down from the hills and began churning and bellowing around in the mud right in front of them. That shut them up. When a hundred and thirty-five bulls come thundering at you down the slopes you couldn't be sure they were going to stop when they reached the flimsy fence. Betty was the only one on that side of the fence, moving the bulls around so everyone could get a good look at them.

The sale only lasted about an hour and a half. The auctioneer pointed out that those bulls, fattened up for the hamburger market, were worth twelve hundred dollars each. He sold them off in lots of ten for a flat rate of eight hundred and fifty dollars each. Betty led them into the yards with an armful of hay and I closed the gate when the yards were full. The stock trucks backed up to the ramp and took them away, and by the end of the following day there wasn't a bull left on the place. It was strangely quiet all of a sudden. Almost eerie, after the racket that had pervaded the atmosphere around there for so long.

Betty and I sat at a wobbly table in the old homestead kitchen with mugs of tea and discussed the future. After paying what she owed she'd made nearly a hundred thousand dollars from her bulls. She'd also had an offer for the station and she was going to accept it and get into a small business in town. A tearooms, making and selling cakes and sandwiches. It's what she'd always wanted to do.

You had to admire that woman's guts. Her ambition had been to run a tearooms in the town and she'd achieved it by hand-rearing a dirty big mob of bulls on some of the hardest and most isolated country in the land. Bloody good luck to her. A few weeks later I saw her off with all she owned loaded into her old Holden station wagon and I've never seen her since. I presume she succeeded in whatever she took on, if she didn't it wouldn't have been from her not having what it takes.

I had to move away from there myself. The new owners wanted to turn the station into a hunting and fishing area for the tourists and they didn't want me there disturbing the hunting. By the time I left the regeneration process had resumed and you could hardly see where a bull had been.

21
BUSH HAPPY

I suppose every era has its share of human flotsam, like the old bloke left behind living in his little hut after the timber mill goes out of business, or the freezing works or the mine closes down. They become reclusive and end up preferring to live alone. Among the bushmen we called it going bush-happy.

Such a one was old Fred, a mate of ours who looked after the Haast cattle track in the days before the road was put through. The track was benched through miles of dense rain forest and it was the only way the South Westland farmers could get their cattle through to the sales.

It was important that the track was kept maintained and that's what Fred did. He cleared the windfalls and slips and kept the drains and watertables clear. He also maintained the single telephone wire that threaded its way along the track on insulators nailed to the trees. And he did a good job. Fred had been a bushman all his life, and he knew no other kind of life. In fact, sadly, Fred was more than a little bush-happy.

It happened to a lot of the old bushmen. They'd spent so much of their time in the bush that they couldn't adjust to anything else and lived out their lives in lonely huts. That's how it was with old Fred. If you were working in the bush with him you'd hardly notice it, but when it came to anything like commerce or ordinary social intercourse he was hopeless.

Fred got paid by the Ministry of Works car that came down to Paringa once a fortnight, every other Thursday. He got his pay in cash in brown paper envelopes which he nailed to the four-by-two framing in his hut. There were dozens of these pay packets around his hut. He paid cash for everything and he'd send an order along to the Bruce Bay store with a twenty-pound note (equivalent to about two hundred dollars today), asking them to send him a pair of strides and the change in tobacco. They always had to fill Fred's orders in judicious proportions. If he sent an order for five pounds' worth of socks they'd send him three pairs and his change. Things like that.

My wife and I were hunting venison around there at the time and got to know old Fred a bit. He was terribly nervous around women and it was something of a break-through when he got talking to my wife about himself and his family. It turned out that he had a daughter with two kids who lived up in Palmerston North. He hadn't seen them for years but he reckoned if anything was wrong they'd have let him know; but we discovered that they didn't even know where he was.

It was probably my wife who talked Fred into making a trip to see his daughter and grandkids before they grew up too much. He had weeks of accumulated leave clocked up and had no trouble getting a fortnight off. He turned up at the store with all his brown pay envelopes in a big brown paper bag and bought a new pair of strides and got a lift on an MOW truck up to Hokitika, from where he was going to fly north.

Four days later he arrived back again, still clutching his big paper bag full of pay packets. He'd got on the plane and flown to Palmerston North and stayed in a hotel. The next day he got a taxi to his daughter's address and saw the kids playing around in the yard and his daughter hanging out the washing. Everything looked all right so he left them there and came away again. And he came by train because the flight up there in the aeroplane had scared the hell out of him.

That's was Fred's last big excursion into the outside world. He stuck to his track and his hut and his brown paper pay packets right up until the Haast road was opened and he was made redundant. I heard that Fred finished his days working as a cowman-gardener on an Otago sheep station, bush-happy as ever.

Joe was another old mate of ours from South Westland who went a bit bush-happy on it. Joe had lived in the bush all his life and minded his own business, then they conscripted him into the army and tried to train him to be a soldier. But they had trouble getting Joe to do what he was told and the first time they let him out on leave he went back into the bush and stayed there. The army decided to make an example of him in case he encouraged other blokes to do the same thing and sent some soldiers to arrest him. But they'd picked on the wrong bloke. Joe got the news that they were coming when they were still fifty miles away. They never saw him.

They sent in teams of soldiers to try and flush Joe out of the South Westland bush but Joe knew the bush and they didn't. They couldn't even find him in it. In fact, he had such an easy time keeping out of their way that he was shooting deer for their hides most of the time, which he swapped with another mate of ours for supplies, booze and money.

The army bods redoubled their efforts to bring this blatant deserter to court martial but they never looked like catching him. One night he was hiding under the hut they were in, listening to them planning how they were going to outwit him. When they went off to look for him in the morning he helped himself to some of their supplies and ammunition and wandered off in the other direction.

After the war they pardoned Joe, who went on shooting for skins the same as he'd been doing all the time. Years later a journalist I knew wrote a book about Joe's adventures hiding out from the army, though Joe himself could never see anything remarkable about it. I wrote a foreword for that book. They took Joe to Auckland for the launching of his book and I ran into him up there. He wasn't happy. There was no way he could fit in there. He was getting into quite a bit of trouble in the bars and there was quick talking and fines to be paid before Joe was

115

safely back in the bush again, where he carried on hunting and prospecting the same as he'd done all his life. Some years later Joe died alone in his hut in full possession of his bush-happiness.

There are hundreds of old blokes around like Fred and Joe. Blokes who worked hard at something all their lives and suddenly it's gone and they can't adjust to anything else. I've got an idea I might end up a bit that way myself, the way things are going.

22

AD LIB

At one stage of it, in my distant youth, I worked from a remote high-country musterers' hut. The weather up there at four and a half thousand feet in the mountains could get pretty hectic at times and there were often days on end when we were confined to the hut, and any kind of reading material was read and re-read many times. In this hut there was a section of a tattered Reader's Digest in which there was an account of an ad lib by a famous English actor. He was acting in a play in England in 1937 and he had to jump over the back of the stage into some water. He was supposed to land on some mattresses but they'd forgotten to put them there and he landed with a loud crash onto the floor behind the stage, and with hardly a pause he called out, "The water, it's frozen!"

At the time I thought that was a pretty sharp bit of thinking, but as time went by I didn't even know I remembered it.

Years later I was working in the city, doing interviews and skits for television and one day one of the other presenters, a bloke called Steve who'd had a bit to do with theatre, dropped a script on my desk and said, "This is a play we're putting on at Christmas. You're the first centurion."

"No way, Steve," I told him. "You'll have to leave me out of it. I can't remember lines. I have to have an idiot-board to do an intro for an interview."

"Don't worry about it," he assured me. "You've only got a few lines, Tom'll go over them with you." And before I could protest any further he hurried off.

It was several weeks until the play went on and I reckoned I'd have plenty of time to convince him that I just wasn't cut out for any kind of acting. Time passed and I didn't get the chance to bail Steve up and tell him he'd have to get someone else to be his centurion. As far as I knew a centurion was some kind of tank they used in wars, but Steve's script described it as a Roman soldier who, in his play, had to inform the chief soldier about an approaching army.

A week before the night of the play we had a rehearsal and I still hadn't been able to talk myself out of the job. It was easy, they said. Nothing to it. Don't worry about your lines Crumpy, there'll be a 'prompt'.

"What the hell's a prompt?" I wanted to know.

"Someone out of sight of the audience in the wings who whispers your lines to you if you forget them," Steve explained.

By this time I realised I was going to have to go along with all this but I was uneasy about the whole thing. The rehearsal went off okay and there was no need for the 'prompt' because we all read our lines off the script. There was quite a bit of excitement in the camp about this play, which we were to perform at the newly opened Mercury Theatre.

Two hours before it was to start we assembled at the theatre and got into costumes. Tights, sandals, cloaks, cardboard swords and spears and hats – the works. It all seemed a bit ridiculous to me. I got into a corner and read my lines over and over until I seemed to know them, but as soon as I tried to remember them without the script I couldn't. A couple of times I tried to tell Steve about my predicament but he was preoccupied with organising everyone and wouldn't listen. Okay, I thought, I did try to warn him.

We lined up in our ridiculous costumes on the stage and in the wings, ready to perform our incredible stunt. The curtain went up and off we went.

The play was about half an hour long and I was to come in half-way through it. It was supposed to be a comedy, but it turned out to be humorous in ways that were never planned for.

First off Wayne dropped a big jar full of coloured water that was supposed to be wine and it broke and splashed all over several of the actors. The broken glass had to be swept into a corner with a flag. Then Colin stood on Barbara's long dress when she was going down some steps and it ripped at the waist and she had to carry on holding it together with one hand. Mike's sword swung between his legs and tripped him and he fell against a big cardboard pillar and brought it crashing down across a trestle loaded with plastic fruit and stuff. It had to be rolled to one side out of the way. The sound-effects got out of sync with the action and there were excited crowd noises while Tom was proposing to Helen and soft flute music behind a sword fight between Tom and Colin.

From where I was waiting in the wings I could hear that the audience was laughing in all the wrong places, and I could see that Steve was getting flustered. He waded manfully on through his lines and actions until it was time for me to make my entrance.

I strode out onto the stage with my big cardboard battle axe and stopped in front of Steve, who was standing at the top of the steps, and saluted. And when I went to speak I didn't know what to say. My lines had vanished out of my head.

I stood there. I could hear the 'prompt' hissing something but I couldn't hear what she was saying. The theatre was silent. Steve and I stood looking at each other for several long seconds, Steve's face was as blank as my mind. Suddenly I said in a loud clear voice, "The water, it's frozen!"

I've seen some hard-case looks on people's faces in my time but never before and never since have I seen a look like the one that came over Steve's face when I involuntarily delivered that immortal stolen line, first uttered by Sir John Gielgud. It was a look of wretched disbelief, as though this couldn't really be happening, as though he was actually somewhere else doing something else. A look of haunted persecution. It was Steve's turn to forget his lines. He turned round twice, looking in the air above everyone's head, as though the solution to the problem might be written there, in the air. Then he said, "Yes, well, we'll just carry on, shall we," which sounded just as ridiculous to me as what I'd just said.

Nobody seemed to know what to do. I remember Helen gathering some spilt plastic grapes, and then Tom picked up the thread of the play, "The legions of Spartacus approach two leagues to the west my liege," he said, or whatever it was I was supposed to have said.

The play blundered on to its miserable conclusion and ended with some polite clapping from the audience. We changed into our normal clothes and forgathered in the lounge bar of the Vic for after-the-show drinks. Steve came over to me and said, "What the hell was that about frozen water, Crumpy? You just about ruined the whole thing!"

"I can't remember lines," I told him.

"Well that's the last time I'm letting you do any acting for me," he said. "You're hopeless. You can't even remember a couple of lines of dialogue!"

"That's what I've been trying to tell you," I said.

"But what the hell's frozen water got to do with a Roman comedy?" he demanded.

"It worked for a famous actor in nineteen thirty-seven," I replied truthfully.

That look started to come over his face again. Then he waved his hand at me and walked away in disgust.

Steve copped a fair bit of ribbing over the dismal failure of his play, and he seemed to have the idea that I was responsible for all of it. There's no justice.

They took our programme off the air and we all drifted away to other jobs, and a few years after that I was offered a part in a television commercial. I needed the money and took the job on. And when I turned up at the studio, who was the director but my old mate Steve from the Town And Around days. It was his first independent directing job and he was being very 'professional' about it.

My lines were simple and just in case I had any trouble with them they had them written on a big piece of cardboard, held up by one of the grips behind the camera. I was dressed up like a medieval prince, tights, ruffled shirt and a crown on my head.

"Action!" said Steve.

I couldn't resist it. I walked in and sat on a throne in front of the camera and waved towards a drape of the Knightsbridge carpet I was supposed to be promoting and said, "The water, it's frozen!"

It was several seconds before Steve recovered sufficiently to say, "Cut!" He was getting that haunted look again.

"That's not funny, Crump," he said.

But I thought it was. In fact I still get a grin on when I remember it.

23

A LONG HAUL

I ran into this bloke in a bar in Sydney, and if you run into a bloke in a bar in Sydney and that bloke's got a problem it's not too long before he's telling you all about it. This bloke's problem was that he needed to get a truckload of drilling equipment from Sydney up to Burketown at the top end of Australia and his driver had gone over to Dubbo on the booze with some shearers two weeks before and hadn't come back. He probably wouldn't turn up at all now.

It just so happened that I was on my way to a place right near Burketown, where I had a camp on a riverbank and a woman waiting for me and, not being one to back away from an adventure, I offered to drive his load of drilling equipment up to Burketown for him.

My first misgivings came next morning when we went out to have a look at his rig. It was a Mickey Mouse outfit if ever I'd seen one. An old long-wheel-base GM truck, loaded with pipes and scaffolding and ropes and boxes and sacks.

"You've got everything you need here," said the bloke, indicating a row of 44-gallon drums behind the cab. "These two are spare gas, this one's your oil and this one's full of water in case you break down. There's a bit of camping gear in those boxes. All you need is your swag and you're right."

My second misgivings came when I was introduced to a bloke who was to accompany me on the trip. He was a grizzled old White Russian called Mick who could only speak a bit of broken English and couldn't drive. He was to do something with the load of gear once we got it up there. I could tell right off that Mick wasn't going to be exactly hilarious company. In fact I had the uneasy feeling that I was going to wish I hadn't taken this on. I was more right about that than I could have guessed.

We had to wait until after dark before we could leave town because the truck wasn't registered. In fact I noticed later that it didn't even have number plates on it. We drove out onto the highway and at dawn we had breakfast in a little town two hundred miles out from Sydney.

I drove on all day. Old Mick sat staring straight ahead, never talking but snorting every now and then. He had this disconcerting habit of snorting back through his nose and it was getting on my nerves. I told him why didn't he blow his nose properly and he explained that he couldn't help it. He'd been kicked in the head by a horse when he was a kid and snorting in through his nose was the only way he could keep his sinuses open. As we drove along I worked out that we were getting one of those snorts every seventeen seconds. It was going to be a great trip!

By that night I'd done enough driving. We stopped by a grove of gum trees and lit a fire and set up our camp, ate sausages and bread, had a pannikin of tea and turned in.

I was tired but I didn't get much sleep that night, or for many nights to come. It was Mick. He'd go off to sleep and after a little while he'd suddenly give this terrific snorting and gasping as though he was choking and half wake himself up and start shouting in Ukrainian, or whatever language he was brought up in. It sounded like a war was going on in his head. There probably was. The shouting would wake him up and he'd snort for a while and then go back to sleep. It got so that the silences in between the choking-to-death and shouting were just as nervewracking as the performance itself. Sleep was out of the question.

It's a big place, Australia. To an Aussie, "up the road a bit" could be anything from two hundred and fifty to twelve hundred miles. What I'm trying to say is that it was a long trip. We had a bit of trouble with the truck. She was burning more than two gallons of oil every day and we ended up putting any waste oil we could scrounge in it. The headlights had packed a sad and I didn't try and fix them because I wasn't happy with the battery. This meant we could only drive in the daytime. We'd blown two tyres and we were running on our last full set. There was a knocking I couldn't identify in the motor but it didn't seem to be getting any worse. We'd spent all the money the bloke had given us for gas and tucker and were now spending mine.

Day after day, trundling along the red, dusty, featureless roads, the only thing that changed was the number on the speedo. Old Mick snorted his way across the continent by day and choked and shouted at night and awoke in the mornings apparently quite refreshed.

I tried shifting away some distance from where Mick was sleeping, but sound travels a long way in the Aussie bush at night, and the choking and shouting were just as disconcerting at two hundred yards as ten yards. I must have slept through some of it from sheer exhaustion but I was becoming a nervous wreck from too much driving and not enough sleep. I'd worked it out that Mick was snorting four times every minute. That was two hundred and forty times every hour. Four thousand seven hundred and sixty times a day Mick would snort that unnerving snort through the back of his nose, excepting, of course, for when he was choking to death and shouting in his sleep.

After more than two weeks of living like that we finally trundled our decrepit rig up through Camooweal and out into the Gulf country. I began to think we might actually be going to make it. Then I had to hitch a ride with a ringer in a ute a hundred miles back to Camooweal to scrounge a piece of radiator hose. That night I slept for twelve hours in the porch of a shed, away from Mick. That blown radiator hose held us up for two and a half days.

My woman was pleased to see me when we finally bounced up to our camp on the riverbank near Burketown. She'd been getting worried about what must have happened to me. I'd been getting worried about what was happening to me too. I was relieved to get the journey over with my sanity intact. It had been a long haul.

We ate a feed and the right thing to do was to invite Mick to stay the night with us, which my woman did.

"No," I told her firmly. "Mick's going on into Burketown. You can follow us in the Land-Rover and bring me back."

I made no apology for this breach of bush etiquette. I got the truck started and drove Mick to Burketown and left him there. He might have been a nice bloke for all I knew, but I was never going to try and sleep within a mile of him ever again if I had anything to do with it.

24

BLACK MAN'S LOGIC

Years ago my woman and I became heroes, quite by accident, to a small tribe of Australian Aborigines. We were working our way around the Gulf of Carpentaria from river to river, hunting crocodiles for a living, and at this stage we were camped on the banks of the Limmin River in Arnhem Land.

We'd been out hunting the night before and got some crocs, and we were scraping the skins on the upturned dinghy in the shallows at the edge of the water, and suddenly we noticed three Abo blokes standing there on the rise above us, standing there in the classical pose, one foot against the other leg and leaning on kangaroo spears in silhouette.

We didn't know about the Abos around there so we moved across to the Land-Rover and clipped a full magazine into the .303 and laid it across the front seat where I could grab it in a hurry if I needed it. Then we waved them over to us. We could smell them; they smeared themselves with dugong fat to keep the sandflies and mosquitoes off them and the smell must have been only just preferable to the insects.

One of them could speak a few mutilated words of English and with the help of some drawings in a patch of sand we gathered that they were camped on a branch of the river one day's walk away and they were being terrorised by 'one bad croc'. It had apparently 'stealed' a young lubra (a girl) and 'bring 'im up and bring 'im down and put 'im in the mangrove'.

"You killem that one," he said.

We decided to have a go at it and loaded up the Land-Rover and drove across the Mitchell Grass plain with the three Abos sitting on the bonnet, guiding us by pointing with their spears.

Just on nightfall we arrived at where about fifty of them were camped among some big paperbark trees in bark humpies. We camped nearby and next day they showed us a slide where the croc had been lying in the mud. It was about twelve feet long by the look of its marks, not a hell of a big one to be taking people.

That night we put the dinghy in the water and loaded the gear into it and paddled off downriver with the only gadget to seriously threaten the crocodile in three hundred million years, a small six-volt spotlight. We missed out on two smaller crocs downstream and returned to the camp, where we lit up the eyes of a big croc in some reeds straight across the river from the blacks' camp. We drifted up to it and stabbed the harpoon into its neck and the blade of the quill went between the vertebrae and severed its spinal cord and killed it instantly. A dead fluke, the only time I ever did that. The easiest big croc I ever got.

We roped the dead croc and towed it across the river to the camp, where we had enthusiastic help to drag it up onto dry ground. The whole camp was gathered around the dead croc in the firelight and we were heroes. The Abos were quite sure it was that bad croc.

The next day my woman and I skinned the croc (you couldn't trust an Abo with a knife around a croc skin, they tend to mutilate them), and while we packed the skin in salt the Abos set about carving steaks off the croc and cooking them. We politely declined to join them and feasted instead on damper and a barramundi we'd caught in our net. We'd eaten the smaller freshwater crocodiles and they're a bit like chicken, but we weren't into noshing up on man-eaters. We found, among other things, a crumpled aluminium frying pan in the belly of that croc.

The Abos couldn't do enough for us after that. We were heroes. We hunted crocs up and down the Limmin and did all right out of it. Our new friends knew where all the crocodiles were. We usually had one or two of them camped with us and they taught us many things about survival in the Australian bush.

It was through those Abos that we learnt something of the degree of misunderstanding that existed between the European settlers and the native inhabitants of Australia. Two men from the tribe arrived back from a year in the Fanny Bay jail in Darwin. One of them had picked up a smattering of English and described their adventures to us.

A year earlier some ringers from a big cattle station and two policemen with trackers had arrived at their camp wanting to know who was responsible for spearing one of their cattle beasts at a water hole and eating it. The two Abos had confessed to stabbing several of them and were taken to Darwin and tried and convicted of cattle stealing, a very serious offence. The magistrate sentenced them to two years in Fanny Bay jail.

They were put in the cool shade of a jail cell and given as much fresh water as they wanted, their food was brought to them, as much flash tucker as they could eat. They even had beer and wine from the pub across the road passed to them through the fence around the jail. In short, they were living in what to them was paradise. There was no struggle for existence amongst the flies and heat and dust of the bush. They were living the life of Riley. After a while they were allowed to wander around the streets for several hours each day, returning to the jail for their evening meal. The odd bit of work they were given to do wasn't work at all to them.

When their sentence was up they were released from the jail and sent off into the desert, back to the comparative hardships of living with their tribe. They'd been model prisoners, done everything they'd been told to do and released early for good behaviour, and they couldn't figure out what they'd done to be evicted from paradise like that, when the magistrate himself had promised them another year of it yet. They genuinely felt cheated.

I explained to them that to a white man what they'd been given was a punishment, and they'd probably get three to five years if they did it again. They laughed. All they had to do was spear a steer and have a feast and then confess to it and get a nice long holiday in Fanny Bay.

We left that region before they re-offended but there was little doubt that they were going to. The white man's punishment was having the very opposite effect to what was intended. I sincerely hope they've got that sort of thing sorted out by now, otherwise there'll be no Abos left out in the bush.

One of the advantages of us being heroes to those Abos was that they confided their bush-lore and misunderstandings with the authorities to us. There was something a bit sad about it all really, the white man's inability to understand the black man's logic, and yet it was logical enough to us. Maybe that magistrate needed to spend a few months out in the bush with them and perhaps even kill a bad croc for them so that he could get to understand the black man's logic.

25

ON THE CUTTING ROOM FLOOR

I've done acting work a few times but I don't enjoy it much, too much waiting around involved. I've always been struck by how remarkably unglamorous filming work is, more boring than anything else. The glamour, if any, always seems to turn up some time later.

In the days when film had to be sent away and processed before they could tell whether or not they'd got what they wanted there was always an atmosphere of anxiety on the job and the directors usually asked for many re-takes, just to make sure they had it 'in the can'. Using extra film was cheaper than having to set it all up again. A thirteen-to-one cutting ratio was considered normal. As well as this you usually had to have a lead from the sound recordist hidden in the shrubbery, up the leg of your pants to a lumpy microphone taped inside your shirt, which severely restricted any movement. The advent of video cameras with instant replay and the tiny radio microphones have removed most of these hassles but it's still a fiddly business as far as I'm concerned.

Notwithstanding all that, there is one acting experience I won't forget in a hurry. Not long back I got roped into doing a short promotional film for New Zealand tourism, working with a famous American television personality called Leeza Gibbons. Crump the Kiwi bushman was supposed to run into this American tourist on the Milford Track and offer to show her a short-cut back to her hotel, but he gets them bushed and they end up on a ledge at the top of the Sutherland Falls, thus showing off some of New Zealand's spectacular scenery. We were working from the tourist hotel at the head of Milford Sound and had to wait around for four days because of dirty weather. Finally the rain stopped and we were able to get on with it.

The first bit went off okay. Leeza walks along through the bush and a dead wild pig crashes down onto the track in front of her, followed by this character with a rifle. They get talking and it turns out that she doesn't know quite where she is. It's getting a bit late in the day so he offers to show her this short-cut he knows about.

Then there came the tricky bit. They put us in a helicopter and dropped us on a tiny ledge at the top of the Sutherland Falls and left us there. I didn't like it. The ledge was about twelve feet wide with two feet of snow on it and the river running through the middle of it, and it sloped over into a sheer three-thousand-foot drop into the valley. There's a lake at the top of those falls and the idea was that the chopper flew across the lake with the camera on the skid and here were these two people standing at the top of the falls and Crump's voice says, "This wasn't here when I came by earlier on."

The chopper disappeared. I'd never trusted those flimsy things and if anything happened to this one we were dead by nightfall. It was freezing cold and we weren't dressed for snow and ice, already our hands and feet were numb. It was a long time before we heard the chopper again, they were off getting the camera rigged up. For the first time in my life I was stricken with what I found out later was vertigo, and that's no fun, believe me. By the time we heard them coming I was propped in the snow, trying not to tip outwards into space.

"Shouldn't you be up on this rock beside me?" suggested Leeza, who was taking this crazy stunt remarkably calmly.

"I'll get up there when that bloody chopper comes past," I replied courageously.

When the chopper approached I made myself get up on the rock beside her and as soon as it had gone past I got down in the snow again, where I felt slightly safer. I wasn't going to get any Oscars for this performance.

They did three more runs, taking about ten minutes over each one, and by the time the chopper returned and hovered to pick us up I was on the verge of total panic. Without waiting for Leeza I chivalrously grabbed a skid and clawed my way into the chopper and told the pilot to get me the hell out of here. I resented him waiting around for her to get in too.

Back at the hotel I had a hot shower and got into warm dry clothes and repaired to the bar and, armed with a double whisky, I was feeling almost human again. Then one of the crew came and told me that they'd been viewing the footage they'd got and it wasn't what they wanted. We were going to have to do it again after lunch.

I laughed at him.

"Like hell," I said. "They're not getting me up there again for all the tea in China, the deer in Fiordland or the trout in Lake Taupo!"

Leeza didn't want to go back up there either, though it was only the cold that put her off the idea. So they decided that they'd have to use stand-ins. Personally I didn't care what they used. A mate of mine who'd come with me on the adventure was about my build and the cameraman's wife was tall and blonde, so after lunch they dressed them up in our gear and flew off with them.

Leeza and I sat in the sun on the hotel balcony yarning. As well as being a good-looker she was an interesting woman to talk to, been all sorts of places and done all sorts of things, but neither of us had ever done anything like we'd done that morning. We'd shared a unique experience and that made us mates. We got along great guns.

The chopper was away for about two hours and when it landed back at the hotel we could see straight away that something hadn't gone quite right. The cameraman's wife was in a hell of a state. They bundled her off to her hotel room where she stayed all afternoon, no doubt getting her wits back into order. I knew exactly what she'd gone through on that tiny ledge at the top of the Sutherland Falls and found it easy to sympathise with her.

They'd dropped them off at the top of the falls and she'd lost her nerve completely. She knelt in the snow clutching my mate's leg and every time the chopper made a run past he had to drag her to her feet and try to make it look as though they were just standing there. She was terrified and panicking and my mate had had trouble keeping her under control. Her panic was contagious and he'd only just managed to keep it together himself.

At dinner that night the cameraman's wife, still a bit shocked, confided to Leeza and me that she'd wanted to throw herself off the ledge to put an end to the ordeal.

"Don't worry mate," I told her. "If I'd thought of that I would have done it myself."

"My hero!" grinned Leeza.

As far as I know that item wasn't shown in New Zealand but someone who'd seen the finished product told me they hadn't used any of the waterfall footage in the finish. After going through all that, my terror had ended up on the cutting-room floor, as they used to describe it in the old days.

No, I'm not that fussed about filming work. I don't like being bored to death any more than being scared to death. They sure earn their money on that caper.

26

BEYOND REPAIR

My wife and I were living in a 1930 Model A Ford car-cut-down-into-a-truck but it wasn't turning out very practicable. At thirty-five miles an hour out on the highway (any more and she'd overheat on you) we were too slow and caused near-accidents from impatient drivers passing in the wrong places. Also, the Model A was too short to sleep comfortably in. We decided to swap it for something more suitable when we moved on next.

We did a winter's possum trapping in the Ruahine Ranges and when the skins went off we exchanged the Model A for an old Volkswagen Combi van and stuck a bunk and everything we owned in it and cruised off for a spell away from smoky huts, maggoty skins and wet bush.

But we didn't cruise far before the motor in the Combi blew up on us. A piston collapsed and scored the bore. We camped for three days in a wrecker's yard outside of town while I stuck a reconditioned motor in the van. Not exactly the change of scenery we'd had in mind.

We set off again and before we'd gone far the gearbox packed a sad. We had to camp in the yard of a disused dairy factory where the weeds grew up through the concrete, while I dropped the motor out of the van and replaced the gearbox with a second-hand one. While I was at it I put new clutch plates and thrust-race in so we wouldn't have any more trouble with it.

For a while after that we only had minor troubles with the Combi but they were continuous. There were electrical

135

problems, like the alternator, the battery, the coil, the windscreen wipers and the dipswitch. The muffler blew out. The petrol tank developed a leak. It was also prone to getting punctures, like four in three days at one stage. All this was proving quite expensive. So far it had cost us more to live in the van than if we'd stayed in a hotel.

We continued on our disrupted travels and the next major mishap we had fortunately happened when we were driving along Ninety Mile Beach. The steering-worm jumped a cog and we lost all right-hand lock. By the time we'd driven down the beach to the road I was getting the knack of steering with only one lock by reversing a number of times at each turn. The drive up the road to Kaitaia was downright nervewracking. The steering box was, of course, beyond repair and we had to get a new one sent up from Whangarei because we couldn't get onto a second-hand one anywhere.

The master-cylinder was the next thing to go, and that led to the whole brake system having to be overhauled. The bloody van was sending us broke. By the time we got back down to Auckland we were having to decide whether to buy an accelerator cable or a wheel bearing, and we couldn't get a warrant of fitness until I'd done a bit of re-wiring and put another headlight in it and one or two other things.

We camped amongst some trees down the bottom of a golf course and got away with it for more than a week while we worked on the van. Then we had a very eventful day happen to us.

First off I was sprung by some early morning golfers shooting a rabbit in a bunker at the thirteenth green and they reported it to a member of the committee. On the same day my wife was caught in the women's changing rooms cleaning the camp oven and washing some clothes. That got reported as well.

The upshot of that was a visit to our camp by two well-dressed blokes on a golf buggy who wanted to know what we were doing there, how long we'd been there and how soon we could get out of there. I had the fuel pump out of the van at the time but we promised to leave as soon as we could get it going. They said that if we were still there the next day they were going to have us removed. Not at all hospitable.

We got away from our golf course camp a few hours later, having replaced or repaired just about every functioning thing on that Combi. We drove to a vehicle testing station, stopping in a shopping-mall car park on the way to re-wire the horn, to have the van checked for a warrant of fitness. It failed the test because of a dangerously rusted-through chassis.

"She's just about falling in half, mate," said a bloke in overalls.

Driving away from the testing station I realised that I'd had a gutsful of that Combi van, but we were stuck with it. It was all we owned and all else we owned was in it. We had under sixty dollars left and no prospects of getting any more money.

I was thinking about all that as we drove along Lincoln Road in Henderson and suddenly I saw a 4 x 4 ute parked outside a Toyota dealership. I pulled up and had a look at it. It had to be a bloody good set of wheels, that.

"Hang on here," I said to my wife.

I went into the dealership office and came out a few minutes later and said to her, "You see that new four-wheel-drive ute there?"

"Yes," she said.

"We'll be in one of our own a month from now," I told her.

I'd asked the dealer who his boss was and if I could ring him up. The boss was a bloke called Brian in Wellington and I told him I'd just seen their new 4 x 4 ute and I'd be prepared to advertise them if they gave me one.

This bloke Brian had more trouble getting over the coincidence of it than I did. I'd caught them just when they were trying to decide on some rugged Kiwi back-country individual to represent their four-wheel-drive range. He was sure we could do a deal. They were anxious to get on with their marketing programme, which included the making of a TV commercial.

The only snag was that not having any fixed abode I couldn't tell the Toyota bloke how to contact me, so I'd given him my brother's address and phone number in Henderson. We drove around to where my brother worked to tell him what I'd done and he said another bloke had been trying to get hold of me about a job. He'd left a phone number. I rang him.

It was Paddy O'Donnell, who became a good friend of ours. He'd just taken over managing one of the Auckland radio stations and wanted me to share the breakfast session with him, for five hundred dollars a week, starting immediately.

We couldn't risk driving around in the van too much with no warrant on it so we camped in the radio station carpark for the first three weeks, by the end of which time I was hosting a midnight-to-dawn talkback show and my wife was operating the panel. It often occurred to me when we were the only ones in the building, running a whole radio station on our own, that it wasn't bad going for a couple of possum trappers from the Ruahine.

Within the month my wife and I took some time off and flew to Wellington where we were put up in a flash hotel and given a smooth car to drive around in. We made the TV commercial in a block of cut-over bush near Wellington and when the filming was done we drove away in a brand-new four-wheel-drive ute with a cheque for two thousand dollars in our kick.

We gave the Combi van to a friend of ours who had no end of trouble with it. Since then we've made several more four-wheel-drive TV commercials. They've been very popular and won a dozen national and international awards.

Now, fourteen years later, I still drive Toyota utes and I still reckon they're great. I came across my old tool box under something in the shed the other day. It brought back memories. I haven't had to carry the tools since the old Combi days. I've probably forgotten how to use them by now.

27

FOUR-WHEEL DRIVE

Not long back I was involved with the Toyota company, advertising their four-wheel-drive utes, and I was quite often called on to demonstrate them for farmers and bush crews and the like. With the vehicles supplied by the company it wasn't long before I discovered what those 4 x 4s would do if they were driven properly, and they kept surprising me with where they'd go. Taking those utes to the limit I had a number of close shaves, but, touch wood, I haven't yet rolled or wrecked one. Traction is the main thing, if you've got traction you can go places that look impossible.

Making the TV commercials had its moments. They had me and my mate Scotty tearing around on washed-out bush tracks, hanging off cranes, flying through the air off ramps, pulling split-second stunts in city traffic, charging through rivers, mud, snow, sandhills and scrub. I once led a parade of Toyota vehicles into the ballroom of the Sheraton Hotel in Auckland with our Olympic champions on board. All great fun.

One of the commercials called for me and Scotty to deliver our lines while travelling up a vertical cliff. This was done by dangling us off a log-hauler winch over a four-hundred-foot papa cliff near Taihape. Neither of us liked the look of the set-up much, the whole contraption hanging on one small shackle. We liked the feel of it even less. It's hard on your neck muscles, trying to talk naturally while sitting and looking straight up at the sky. I don't know about the poor cameraman, he was roped onto a ladder hanging halfway down the cliff.

We had the usual holdups. We'd be halfway through our act when an aeroplane would go over, lousing up our sound, and we'd have to do it again. Or a vehicle would come grinding up the road and we'd have to wait until it was gone. Some of the takes were no good because of the rocks and dirt that showered down on us, dislodged from where the winch rope was dragging over the top edge of the cliff. When Scotty and I did get our bit right there'd be some technical hitch and we'd have to be lowered down to the riverbed and go through the whole unnerving process again. And again.

Scotty, looking in panic at the drop below us: "I say, this is a bit over the top, isn't it Crumpy!"

Crump: "It can get a bit tricky if you run into anyone coming the other way mate."

We were beginning to think we must have the footage they wanted, but the director wanted us to do it once more and they pushed us backwards over the cliff to lower us down again. We were getting a bit used to it by this time. It was beginning to look as though something wasn't going to give out and send us plunging to our deaths on the rocks below after all, but going backwards over the edge was always a bit of a thrill. This time one of the mudflaps caught under one front wheel as we went over and it held the weight of the vehicle for several inches until the three bolts holding the flap onto the bracket pulled out with a bang and we suddenly dropped four or five inches onto the winch rope.

Now four or five inches mightn't seem like much of a drop to you, but I can assure you that it was the longest four inches that Scotty and I ever dropped. This was it, we were dead. They reckon that in dire moments your whole life can flash before you. Well, there was plenty of time for that. Scotty confided to me later that he'd had heaps of time to wish he'd been nicer to his mum.

With the vestiges of artificial confidence we'd manage to build up completely dispelled by the incident we weren't making a very good job of our acting and they finally decided to go with what they had, and the ad turned out to be a great success. I wouldn't want to have to do that one again though.

Another close one that happened was probably much more dangerous than that. I was living up this valley where the road followed one side of the river and my hut was on the other side. I'd found that by shifting the air intake on the ute I could boot it across the river with the water surging up around the windscreen wipers. Much deeper and swifter than you could ever have got across on foot, and much deeper and swifter than the manufacturers had ever allowed for.

I'd come across to my hut the day before with some gear and supplies and in the night it started raining heavily. The river was going to come up in flood but I didn't need to go out again for a few days so I didn't bother taking the ute back over to the road. There was a swingbridge about half a mile up the river that I could use if I had to get out during a flood.

It was still raining steadily the next day and I was sitting peacefully in front of my open fire writing when I heard a pounding on my door above the sound of the rain on the roof. I opened the door and there was a white-faced young Maori bloke standing there in a drenched Harris Tweed overcoat that must have weighed as much as a half-grown pig.

"Alan's shot himself up Blacks Creek," he blurted, then he ran off into the rain. I never saw him again and heard later that the police were looking for him over something or other.

Alan was a neighbour who had a small farm on the other side of the valley further down. He'd been having a bit of trouble with his missus and I didn't know whether he'd shot himself on purpose or accidentally or how bad it was, but going by the state that young bloke had been in it was obviously some sort of emergency.

I got into my Swanndri and gumboots and ran out and drove the ute down to the river to see what it was like. I had fifty posts on the back that I hadn't unloaded because of the rain, and it was probably very lucky that I hadn't. It was the weight that probably saved my bacon. The river was a banker, flooded and rising, with driftwood and logs floating past. If I'd hesitated I wouldn't have tackled it. I was still in four-wheel-drive from coming across the day before, so I dropped her into low second and booted her out into the current.

The track into the river on the other side was about two hundred yards downstream with a shingle bar down the middle of the river which was about fifty yards wide at that point. There was no shingle bar to be seen now, just surging brown waves of water with sticks and branches and logs swirling around in it. I angled out to where the shingle bar usually was and began to nudge my way across the current with the water up to the windows.

Every now and again the current grabbed the ute and threatened to turn it round but each time I got a bit of traction on the stones and managed to straighten it up, revving the guts out of it. There was a patch of easier going when I got onto the shingle bar but when I went to boot it up onto the track and out of the river on the far side the water had washed out a channel and I was swept past it.

This was serious. Forty yards downstream there was a big hole in the corner of the river where I used to catch the odd trout. If we got into that we were going to roll over and get buried in the shingle somewhere downstream. I could only steer her towards the bank and feed her the fat, and that Toyota ute bounced and banged its way through some boulders and across the channel and clawed its way up an impossible shingle bank and out onto a small flat covered with manuka. This was no time to slow down, I crashed through the scrub and up another rise, flat-tack through a bit of a swampy place and then out through my neighbour's fence and onto the road, where I stopped for a moment and thumped the steering wheel of that ute and said to it, "You bloody beaut!"

I found Alan. He'd crawled out to the road at Blacks Creek. They'd been hunting and Alan had been sliding down a bank into the creek when he'd got out of control and his rifle had

142

discharged. The bullet had gone down through the top of his thigh, out through the back of his thigh and into the calf and out through the front of his leg. Four large-calibre bullet holes in his leg. I tore up his wet shirt and bandaged him up to stop the bleeding and took him into town in record time. After leaving him at the Opotiki Hospital I stopped at the pub and downed two stiff whiskies. It was still raining.

"How did you get out Crumpy?" said a bloke I knew. "That river of yours is in flood, isn't it?"

"Nothing the ute couldn't handle," I said nonchalantly.

Alan was okay. The bullet had missed his bones and within a few days he was back on deck. Everyone in the valley reckoned it was a bit of a miracle how he'd been so lucky, but I happened to know that that wasn't the only bit of a miracle that had happened in the valley that day.

28
THE WRONG JOKE

I got to know this bloke called Don whose business was organising conferences for companies and organisations and he used to get me to put on an act for him now and again. He paid me well and I didn't have to do a hell of a lot. I had this stunt. I'd get them to put a false set of doors on the conference room and when the conference members were all seated in there I'd crank up a chainsaw with a bit of extra oil in the mixture to make some smoke and cut my way in, cutting upwards through the doors so the wood chips flew out into the room. Up one side, across the bottom, up the other side, across the top, kick the panel in and walk into the room, stop the saw and dump it on the nearest table, go to the microphone and tell them a joke. They never knew whether the place was being raided or what the hell was going on and it was always easy to get them laughing. After that I'd mingle among them a bit, give a bit of cheek, collect my cheque and drift off to wherever I was living at the time.

On one of these jaunts Don wanted me to go down to Queenstown and do my stunt at a conference of staff members of some big manufacturing outfit. They'd been told that a surprise mystery guest was going to turn up sometime during the conference.

I got to the venue early and had the false door installed and the chainsaw jacked up and hidden in a handy cupboard. The guests arrived and the opening session of the conference was under way and Don and I sneaked a look through a side door so

I could see what the set-up was in there before I had to go in. There were a hundred or more of them and their managing director was standing on a small stage at a microphone telling everyone what a grand bunch of workers they'd been that year. They were already starting to fidget and cough, he was obviously one of those people who didn't know when he'd said enough.

I'd decided on the joke I was going to tell them, it was innocuous enough. A bus pulls up outside the Huapai pub and the driver goes in and tells the publican that he's got a busload of harmless mad people and they're thinking of letting them out into society and wanted to check on how they went in the pub. Bring 'em in, says the publican. They're no good with money, warns the bus driver, just take anything they give you and keep a tab of it and I'll square you off when we leave. Not a problem, says the publican, and all these mad people file into the bar and start ordering drinks.

A couple of hours later the bus driver comes in and orders everybody back onto the bus and they file out and get on the bus. How did you get on with 'em? the bus driver asks the publican. Not a problem, says the publican. They're better-behaved than some of my normal customers. How did you get on for money? asks the bus driver. The publican laughs, I've got a plastic bucket full of buttons and safety pins and bus tickets and bottle tops and bits of string and paper and all manner of stuff. It comes to two hundred and thirty dollars all together.

Have you got any change for this dust-bin lid says the driver, holding one up.

That was my joke.

Sitting on a chair on the stage beside the managing director there was a woman giving all sorts of hand signals and mouthing as he talked.

"What's that woman there up to?" I whispered to Don.

"They employ a lot of deaf and dumb people," he explained. "They're some of their most valuable workers. She's passing on what the boss is saying to them."

Just then the boss finally finished his speech and announced that it was time to introduce the surprise mystery guest they'd been promised. This was my cue to make my entrance. I cranked up the chainsaw, cut through the door, booted out the panel, dumped the saw on a handy table in front of two couples, strode up to the microphone in my Swanndri and hat and welcomed them to the conference.

My audience was a bit quiet, which I suppose was only to be expected in the circumstances. The woman was still sitting there beside me, translating my words into signals, and then, to my horror, I heard myself say that a bus pulls up outside the Huapai pub and the driver goes in and tells the publican that he's got a busload of deaf and dumb people out there and can they come in for a while.

I didn't even know I knew a joke about deaf and dumb people in a pub, but somewhere in the distant past I must have heard one, and there was nothing I could do but carry on and hope the punch-line wasn't too bad. So I ploughed manfully on through this joke, with the woman gesticulating along beside me.

This bloke wanders into the Huapai pub and tells the publican he's got a busload of deaf and dumb people out there and is it okay if they come in for a while. The publican says sure, and the bus driver explains that while they can't actually talk to him they're very intelligent and they'll indicate the drinks and the size of glass they want. They're okay with money and there shouldn't be any problems. Bring 'em in says the publican, and all these deaf and dumb people file into the bar. I can't drink, says the driver, I'm driving. I'll be out in the bus if you want me.

A couple of hours later the publican comes out to the bus, where the driver is dozing off under his newspaper. The publican taps on the newspaper and wakes the driver. What's wrong? he says. They're indicating the drinks they want, says the publican, and there's no trouble with the money or anything, but they've suddenly all started yawning. Yawning?

says the driver – blast it, they've started singing, we'll never get the bastards out of there now!

While this was sinking in to the bemused audience there were a few moments of silence which I can only describe as soul-blistering. Then they started cracking up and the whole place erupted in laughter that went on for minutes.

Whew!

During the function that followed I discovered that the company workers were very fond of and protective of their deaf and dumb mates. It was quite touching how they regarded and respected each other and a good example of how the inclusion of handicapped people in the workplace can and should be. We all ended up having a great time.

So, by and large, my mission had been accomplished as well as anyone could have expected. My part in it was over. The next day they were going on jet-boat and helicopter.

The next morning at breakfast in the hotel Don suddenly said, "By strike, Crumpy, that joke you told yesterday was a bit close to the bone wasn't it!"

"It was the best way to get 'em relaxed mate," I said. "It worked okay didn't it?"

"It worked all right," he agreed, "but I wouldn't have risked it myself."

I didn't bother to tell him that I wouldn't have risked it either, not for the whole conference budget.

29

THE DOG
BLOKE

I was doing a rural delivery run in a country district, three days a week and the rest of the time to myself. We delivered most things to places on the run, a kind of general service to the area, and once I got the hang of it and knew where everything was it was a bit of a cushy number. We sometimes carried passengers and one day this bloke turned up at the depot with two suitcases and two big black-and-tan dogs that looked like they might have a bit of beardie in them. I told the bloke I could only carry the dogs if they were in crates or cages.

"We carry quite a bit of foodstuffs," I explained.

"What about in sacks?" said the bloke.

"I don't know if I want to cart dogs in sacks," I said dubiously.

"They travel like that a lot," the bloke assured me. "Get a couple of sacks, I'll show you."

I found some sacks for him and he shook one out on the floor of the van and held the end open and told one of his dogs to "get in there". The dog jumped up and nosed his way into the bottom of the sack and curled up with a flop onto the floor. The bloke shoved him across the floor out of the way and repeated the process with the other dog.

"It gets a bit cold in the winter where I come from," he explained. "The dogs often travel that way on the utes and that."

So we took off on the run with two dogs in sacks among the mailbags and boxes and parcels in the van. The dog bloke sat beside me. He was going to a station out at the end of the run, where he had a job jacked up.

"Any pig hunting around?" he asked, waving at the expanse of scrub and bush on either side of the road.

"Yep," I said. "There's a lot of pig hunters around here."

"Don't talk to me about bloody pig hunters," snorted the dog bloke. "They're the worst bloody thing that ever happened to the bloody bush."

As an ardent pig hunter myself (I was only in the area for the pig hunting) I was curious to know why he was so fired-up about pig hunters.

"How do you make that out?" I enquired.

"You've just got to look at the bloody dogs they take into the bush with them," he said. "They turn up with a dirty big pack of scoffing yeller bloody mongrels that jump off the truck and go romping off through the bush, hunting for themselves. If they do ever stumble across a pig worth eating they've usually chewed the meat to bits before anyone can get there. Then they'll hool something across to the next watershed and they've lost them. They quite often end up going home without them and spend days trying to find the bloody things again. In the meantime they've loused up the hunting in a whole valley for weeks."

"It's not always like that," I protested.

"It's like that too bloody often for my liking," said the dog bloke.

"We get a lot of pigs around here," I told him. "And we've got some pretty good dogs too."

"You might have," conceded the dog bloke, "but for every good dog in the bush there's ten bloody meat-scoffin' mongrels."

There was nothing much I could say to that. We drove along in silence for a while, made a couple of deliveries, then the dog bloke said, "There's only two types of hunting dogs you need to think about."

"What's that?"

"There's dogs that know what they're doin' and dogs that don't. Dogs that don't know what they're doin' hunt by instinct. You're lucky if you get any good meat with them. They're a menace, they're stupid, they'll get ripped up, they'll worry sheep, they're more bloody trouble than they're worth."

He shut up for a while and then I said, "What about the other sort? The sort that knows what they're doing?"

"That's a different story," he said. "A dog that knows what he's doing is hunting for you. He rounds the pig up and if it's dangerous he'll bail it. If it beats him he'll let it go. If he can hold it he will. He's never away finding for too long and he never gets lost. And if you need any more than two dogs to catch pigs some of 'em are no good."

"What sort of dogs do you use then?" I asked him.

"Good ones," he said. "Dogs that know what they're doing."

We stopped to put a mailbag and a box and a prescription in a mailbox and I suggested to the dog bloke that his dogs might like to hop out and stretch their legs and get a breath of fresh air.

"Nar, don't disturb them. They're quite comfortable."

As though to back him up one of the dogs inside his sack hitched himself around a bit and grunted contentedly. We drove on for a while and then the dog bloke spoke again.

"I've seen 'em all," he said. "Bull-mastiffs, bull-terriers, wolfhounds, great danes, airedales, boxers, foxies, greyhounds, corgies and all the bloody mixtures. One in a hundred might turn out okay, the other ninety-nine are useless for anything to do with hunting."

The dog bloke went on about dogs. How he'd seen 'em hunting with a french poodle and a fat old rottweiler. He'd seen 'em try alsatians, basset hounds, spaniels, labradors, ridgebacks, whippets, setters, pointers and dalmatians, all running round in the bush, and all of them bloody useless.

"They're not all like that," I repeated. "We've got some pretty good dogs around here."

"What sort of dogs do you use, anyway?" he asked.

"Good ones," I told him. "My dogs know what they're doing."

"How many of 'em ya got?"

"Two."

"What breed are they?"

"Working dogs. Collies. Heading dogs."

That rocked him.

"You hunt pigs with them?" he asked.

"Sure. All the time. I also work sheep and cattle with them."

"Do you get plenty of pigs?"

"Not always," I said.

That shut the dog bloke up for a while. He seemed to be thinking about something, and then he said, "When are you going out hunting next?"

"Tomorrow morning," I told him. "I've got permission to hunt on a block at the back of one of the farms that hasn't been hunted for a long time."

"How about taking us out with you," he asked. "Me dogs need a run."

I thought it over for a while and then said, "No thanks, mate. I wouldn't really mind but, you see, I'm about a bit fussy about what sort of dogs I take out hunting with me."

That shut him up for the rest of the trip, which suited me. This bloke had all the earmarks of a fanatical pig hunter, and fanatical pig hunters talk of little else but dogs and pigs and they'll punish your ear on the subject for as long as you'll let them. I know, I'm one of them.

I took the dog bloke up to the station where he was going and he called his big black and tan dogs out of their sacks and they crawled forth and jumped down off the van, shook a cloud of dust off themselves and cocked their legs in turn on a gate post. The dog bloke thanked me (I didn't ask him to pay for the trip) and went off up the path with his two suitcases and his dogs sloping along behind him.

I was right about the dog bloke, Eric. He was still around there when I left the district a few months later. He did general

152

work around the station and hunted pigs every bit of free time he got. He turned out to be not a bad sort of a bloke when you got to know him a bit. I took him out with me a few times and guess what? – his dogs weren't all that good. They'd find close and grab a pig for him, but they were inclined to bark on the trail, they were clumsy and got in the way and caused one of my dogs to get ripped by a boar. They were also under some suspicion over some dead lambs they'd found and the boss had told Eric to keep his dogs on the chain or they'd get the bullet. Eric thought they were crackerjacks, but I wasn't all that impressed by them.

I never made any comments to Eric about his dogs. It would have been a waste of time. Dog blokes usually have no trouble identifying the shortcomings of anyone else's dogs, and yet have a curious inability to see the faults in their own. I know, I'm a bit of a dog bloke myself.

30

A SOFT
TOUCH

I like merino mutton, always have, and when I had a few acres of my own at one stage of it I got myself a small flock of merinos and once they started breeding I drafted out sixteen wether hoggets for mutton for the house. I was quite pleased with the results.

Rather than dog the killers into the yards and butcher them there I used to drive the tractor into the paddock, pick out the one I wanted and shoot it. They died without being stirred up and nervous and the mutton was always deliciously tender. This worked perfectly up to the point where I'd whittled them down to seven.

Through a series of events, and being a soft touch, I ended up with two young Maori kids living with me. They liked the farm life and the animals and soon had their chores to do around the place. It was still winter and one of their jobs was to feed the muttons and before long the sheep were following the kids around. I enjoyed seeing them up there in the paddock, waist-deep in woollies. The quieter the sheep the better the mutton.

This went on for about a month and then when it was time to do another sheep for mutton I took the kids up the paddock to get one. Part of their education, I thought, but it was me who was about to be educated.

As soon as we entered the paddock the sheep came running up to see what the kids had for them to eat. This was going to be easy. I didn't even need the rifle, I could just grab one and cut its throat.

"That one there will do us," I said, steeling my knife.

"You're not killing Henry," said young Hikuera, looking horrified.

"Henry?" I said.

"We're not eating Henry," said little Missy positively.

"All right," I said. "We'll do this one here."

"But that's Sam!" protested Hikuera.

"He's going to kill Sammy!" wailed Missy.

"Okay, okay," I said. "We won't kill Sammy. We'll do that ugly one over there."

But that was Freddy.

In turn I tried each of the other sheep but they turned out to be Buddy, Winston, Nohi and Bunty. There was no way those kids were going to eat any of those muttons. They'd named them after people they knew who they reckoned they looked like. We went back down to the house empty handed.

We went into town that day for supplies and I bought some meat from the butcher for the first time in more than a year. I sure didn't like having to pay for it when I had better mutton running around at home. The kids didn't mind eating the meat from the butcher's but there was no way they'd have eaten any of those fat, spoilt merino hoggets in our own paddocks. This was ridiculous. I decided to try another tack.

"Mr Redpath wants to swap one of his romney hoggets for one of our merinos." I told the kids at breakfast one morning.

They went on scooping Weetbix into their little faces as though they hadn't heard me.

"We'll take one of ours over to Redpaths after I drop you kids off at the school bus and kill one of theirs for mutton for us," I said. "A bit of romney'll make a nice change."

"You don't like romney," stated Hikuera.

"He's going to kill one of the sheep!" cried Missy.

"No I'm not," I lied. "I'm just going to swap one of ours for one of Mike's."

"You're only saying that," said Hikuera accusingly. "You're going to kill one of our sheep and say it's Mr Redpath's."

Missy started sulking and blubbering. "He's going to kill Henry," she sobbed.

I tried to bluff my way through it but the kids refused to get in the ute to go to school until I'd promised not to do any sheep-swapping that day.

It went on, and it was ridiculous. Here were two young kids holding me to ransom over my own sheep. I was buying mutton from the butcher because I didn't want to have to explain my predicament to any of my neighbours. In the meantime Hikuera and Missy kept swiping sheep nuts out of the bag in the woolshed and stuffing the killer hoggets with them, though there was by now more grass in their paddock than they could eat.

The situation was resolved somewhat when Hikuera's mother returned from the season as a fleeco on a shearing gang down south and he shifted back in with her in town. Missy went with him and ended up living with her aunt and uncle down the coast.

By this time my seven hoggets were rolling in fat. Too fat for eating, and I had to put them out on the hill until they lost a bit of condition. They'd been reprieved by two young kids.

A man's a bit of a soft touch, I suppose, but I'd learnt not to let anyone give a name to any animal you want to eat.

Not long after all that young Hikuera, who was seven years old, pestered everyone until we let him come out and stay with me for the school holidays. I was writing a novel about an old bloke and his young Maori nephew at the time. I'd write in the mornings and in the afternoons we'd do a bit of stock work with the horses and dogs, or put the hinaki in the river to catch an eel, or cut a load of firewood, or wait up in the bush with the shotgun to try and ambush the cunning old harrier hawk that was stealing our chickens, or maybe go somewhere. Anything we did seemed to be okay with Hikuera. He was a good little bloke to have around and liked learning things. Not long before he arrived this time I'd swapped half a dozen merino muttons (including Henry, Sammy, Freddy, Buddy, Winston and Nohi)

157

with one of the neighbours for a bullock, which we'd butchered in the yards and cut up for the freezer. I'd thrown the bullock's head out into the paddock for the dogs to chew on. There's quite a lot of meat on a bullock's head.

Hikuera came running into the kitchen, where I was writing at the kitchen table.

"There's a cow's head in the paddock!" he said breathlessly.

"It's a bullock's head," I said absently. "Don't touch it."

"Why?"

"It has to say there until all the bad thoughts it's ever had have come out of its nose," I told him.

"The dogs must be getting bad thoughts," he said logically. "They eat it."

"It doesn't work with dogs," I said. "Only people."

"When do we know when all its bad thoughts have gone?" he wanted to know.

"When the bottom jaw comes off it," I said.

"What do we do then?"

"We bury it. Just don't go near it in the meantime or you'll catch bad thoughts."

I don't know why I told him all that, the truth would have worked much better, but I was preoccupied at the time with what I was doing. Making stuff up.

A couple of days after that I was writing away at the kitchen table and glanced up through the window and saw young Hikuera with the egg bucket coming back across the paddock from feeding the chooks and ducks. He had his hill-stick, which we'd cut in the bush for him and he carried it everywhere.

The dogs had been dragging the bullock's head around and it was lying, propped up on one horn, on the ground just outside the gate into the yard around the house. As he approached the head Hikuera slowed down, stopped and stared at it for a while and then cautiously poked it in the nostril with the end of his stick. The head must have been finely balanced and it slowly tipped upright. The egg bucket went one way, the stick the other way and Hikuera shot through the gate, landed with a bang on the porch and dashed into the kitchen.

"It moved!" he shouted.

"What moved?" I said.

"The head. It moved!"

"You must have touched it," I said. "I told you to leave it alone."

"I only touched it with my stick," he said.

"Well we'll have to burn that stick now," I told him. "We'll cut you another one later. And remember not to touch that head again."

There was no need to tell him that. Whenever he had to go past that bullock's head after that he walked in a wide circle around it.

A few days after the stick incident Hikuera dashed into the kitchen and announced that the bottom jaw had come off the head. All its bad thoughts had gone. We took the spade and dug a hole and buried the remains of the bullock's head behind the shed.

I thought that would be the end of the matter but not long after that Hikuera's mum and two of her mates came out to the farm to gather watercress and kawakawa and when we were sitting in the kitchen having a cup of tea Hikuera told them all about the bullock's head and the bad thoughts coming out of its nostrils.

The three women were looking at me across the table.

"I was just having him on," I stammered.

"He was just kidding you, boy," said Hikuera's mum, grabbing him and giving him a cuddle.

The look young Hikuera gave me across that table taught me not to try and have kids on in the future. It can backfire on a bloke.

A few months after that Hikuera, now eight years old, spotted my ute parked outside the pub on his way home from school. He ambushed me and asked if he could come out to the farm for the holidays.

"No mate," I told him. "I've sold the farm, I'm moving on. It's been tying me down too much. I'll be gone from round here in a couple of weeks."

He looked at me with deep suspicion. "Are you bullock-heading me?" he said.

"No Hik," I said. "I wouldn't do that to you."

"You did that time," he pointed out.

He probably only really believed me when I called in to their place to say goodbye on my way out of the district. His mother thanked me for having taken Hikuera under my wing, but I reckoned we were square enough, young Hikuera and I.

31

NO
TROUBLE

The other day a woman I know was going crook about some hassles she'd had with an Indian taxi driver, and I was reminded of an adventure I had with another Indian taxi driver in another place.

It was in New Delhi, I was passing through that city and had a bit of time to fill in so I rang up an old friend who lived there and arranged to go out to his place. I was looking forward to seeing him again. He lived in Gundai Street in a suburb called Rosebank.

I had no idea where Rosebank was so I decided to get a taxi and found one parked by the kerb on a city street. I asked the driver if he knew where Rosebank was and he assured me that no trouble, sir, he not only knew where Rosebank was, he knew the very street I wanted. His grandmother lived there, his father was born there, his sister's husband had a business there and his wife's uncle was assistant headmaster at the Rosebank Primary School. Looked quite promising at this stage.

He leapt from the cab and called me sir and sat me in the passenger's seat with great ceremony. I noticed that the back seat was taken up by two spare wheels, a gear box and some other bits on a sack on the floor and boxes and clothes piled on the seat. The windscreen was badly cracked and criss-crossed with insulation tape. There was no window on my side at all. The upholstery was coming apart in several places and a tangle of electrical wire hung down from under the dash. The car was a wreck.

While I was noticing all this the driver had crossed the road and was talking with three young blokes who were standing there. They came over to the taxi. The driver crouched in the open door, fiddling with wires under the dash. Then he hopped in and slammed the door twice and pumped the clutch and gear lever and shouted to the three young blokes, who began to push the taxi along the road. Even at this pace the vehicle rattled and creaked.

After several attempts at jump-starting it the motor fired, enveloping the three pushers in a cloud of blue smoke. By revving the clapped-out motor and slipping the clutch to avoid stalling, my worthy driver gradually gained momentum and we moved clear of the cloud of smoke we were putting up and trundled off along the street.

We weaved our way through the teeming city streets and out into the suburbs, where the roads became worse and worse. Then the taxi stopped.

No trouble, sir, my driver assured me. We just needed some petrol. If I could let him have a few rupees we could get some from just along here. The petrol man was his sister-in-law's cousin.

I gave him twenty rupees and he went off up the road toward some shops. I sat in the dilapidated taxi and meditated on the vicissitudes of travel in these faraway places.

My driver returned with a plastic container of gas and I gave him a hand to pour it into the tank through a rolled-up piece of cardboard. Then I noticed that one of the rear tyres was flat.

No trouble, sir. We have a spare wheel.

All we had to do was change one bald, cracked tyre for another. There was no jack. We put some blocks of wood and a book under the back axle, loosened the burred wheel-nuts with a chewed-out old tube spanner and dug a hole in the dirt road under the flat tyre with a broken spring-leaf.

When we had the hole big enough we took the wheel off and bolted the other one on and filled the hole in as much as we could, but now we couldn't get the car off the blocks.

No trouble, sir. We can dig another hole under the wood.

It wasn't easy but we managed to dig the blocks out, which left the car with one wheel sitting in the soft dirt in the hole we'd dug under it. We couldn't move the car to start it.

No trouble, sir. My cousin lives near here. He can tow us.

And with that my resourceful driver, whom I'd begun to call No Trouble in my mind, sloped off up the road, leaving me standing there with my best strides covered with dirt and grease on my shirt from digging under the taxi. I had no idea where I was and the people going up and down the road were looking at me as though I was something from another planet. I sat in the taxi where I was less conspicuous and meditated on the attributes of Indian taxi drivers.

My driver returned about half an hour later on the back of a motor bike driven by an old woman.

No trouble, sir. My cousin is up this way. We'll be back in a few minutes.

And off he went again. By this time I'd spent more time sitting in his taxi stationary than moving. Another half hour went by. I was getting a bit hacked-off with all this. If I'd seen another taxi I'd have stopped it, but none came past. Then No Trouble and his cousin arrived back in a three-ton blue and yellow truck with high sides and adorned with emblems and ribbons and badges. It also had shot injectors and belched great plumes of black smoke into the air. An impressive machine!

After some consultation they backed the truck up to the taxi and tied a rusty wire rope onto it and with much shouting and a burst of smoke and a snap of the neck we were plucked out of the hole and dragged off up the road.

The taxi held together but it wouldn't start. After about a hundred yards they stopped, consulted, raised the bonnet and discussed whether or not it was the coil giving trouble. It was getting plenty of gas, you could smell it. They began to talk of going off in the truck to get another coil off someone they knew.

"Look mate," I said to No Trouble. "Where's this Rosebank? I want to get there."

"No trouble, sir," said No Trouble. "This is Rosebank. Gundai Street."

I looked around.

"Where's number two hundred and twelve?" I asked.

"No trouble, sir. It's just along there on the other side."

I looked back along the street. I could see where we'd dug the hole in the road to change the wheel, where I'd sat in the taxi and waited for over an hour, a hundred and fifty yards from where I was going.

"Why didn't you tell me it was so close?" I demanded. "I could have walked here."

I was then told with great dignity that No Trouble was a professional taxi driver. It was his job to get me there and my job to pay him, and maybe a generous tip if I was very pleased with the service.

I wanted to pay him off and walk along to where I was going but he wouldn't hear of it. He had to get me there in his taxi. It was a matter of professional pride.

After further consultation we reached a compromise. I got back in the taxi with No Trouble and the cousin towed us along to my destination with the smoking blue and yellow truck.

As I paid off the intrepid No Trouble I felt a surge of affection for him and added a generous tip. After all, we'd been through so much together, No Trouble and I.

32

ON FIRE

I was more than fifty years old when I first got the power on in a place I owned and began to use an electric stove. I'd rented places that had electric stoves and even gas ones but it happened that I always seemed to have a woman around who did the cooking. I suspect myself of not wanting to learn how to use the things, but the fact remains that when I finally got an electric stove of my own I didn't know how to use it and I burnt just about every meal and pot. The only utensil that survived my introduction to the electric stove is my old cast-iron camp oven, and I scraped a lot of burnt tucker out of that before I got the hang of that stove.

The main reason for all that is my lifelong love of fire. It's great stuff! I've used wood-burning stoves but I always leave the firebox open so that I can actually see the fire and they don't operate properly like that. But I'll cook you anything you like over an open fire. I'm told that to this day more people cook their food over open fires than by all other means put together. Good on 'em!

There's something comforting about fire that takes a lot of beating. No hut or camp in the great outdoors ever comes alive until the fire's going. Even when the chimney smokes and you can hardly see or breathe in the hut no one dreams of putting the fire out.

In many situations the ability to get a fire going can be a matter of life or death. Keeping your matches dry in the bush has always been very important for survival. Wax matches were greatly favoured when they were available because of them being almost water-proof, but they were taken off the market when they were found to be a hazard to the pine forests. Too easy to accidentally start a bush fire with. After they were gone we used to dip the wooden matches in varnish to make them easier to keep dry. You could always strike one on a pane of glass.

In some of our camps we used to burn more than a ton of rata driftwood from the river bed in a single night. Big, warming, glowing, leaping flames, sending showers of sparks spiralling up into the night sky like released extra stars whenever we threw another man-sized log into it. Ah, those were the fires!

Rata is my favourite firewood, though there's a native wood that burns even hotter than rata and that's from a tree called the black miro. That stuff will burn the back out of your chimney or the grate out of your stove but it's not as commonly found throughout the New Zealand bush as the rata, which burns bright and clean and hot.

One of the first things you learn when you live in the bush is what burns good and what doesn't. Four of us got bluffed when we were caught out for the night high in thick bush on Manuohau in the Ureweras. Just on dark we found what we thought was a fallen totara log and decided to spend the night there. It was a memorable night, that one. The log we chipped our wood out of wasn't totara but a tree with similar looking wood, the kaiwaka. The difference is that totara burns well and kaiwaka doesn't, it chars and blackens but won't take fire and build up a heat. We froze, and learnt.

After a lifetime of mucking around with fire I built a fireplace and chimney on a hut I had that I reckoned would be ideal. The fireplace was four feet wide and three feet deep, concrete, with a gate hinge set into it to swing billies and camp ovens further from or closer to the fire. It worked well and I had a lot of satisfaction from it, not the least from observing how other people reacted to it.

There are people who are attracted to fire and people who aren't, and it's real easy to tell one from the other. You put them in a room where there's an open fire burning. The non-fire person will display no unusual behaviour, they sit down and carry on as normal. The fire-person, on the other hand, man or woman, will, when confronted by the naked flames of an open fire, lose all their self-control. The first thing they do is grab the poker and dig your fire in the ribs with it. Then they'll put more wood on it, arranged the way it ought to have been. After that they stand with their back to the fire until their pants get so hot their legs get burnt, but that never stops them. They just can't leave the fire alone. They're funny to watch, they can't help themselves.

And I can't talk, I'm one of the worst fire-pokers and hoggers. For more than forty years I've spent an average of more than four hours each day hunkered over open fires. Twenty-eight hours a week, a hundred hours a month, twelve hundred hours a year. That's around fifty thousand hours I've spent staring into the flames and I'm still not tired of it. Give me some wood and a lighter and I'll cook you back from a good big fire as quick as I can build it up.

This poem I wrote about fire might explain a bit about this strange affliction.

FIRE

O Fire, what message have you imparted
To my vacant mind
As I stared those thousand hours
Into your gesticulating flames?

What wisdom have you whispered
To my unguarded ear
In your snapple and crack
And your muttering blaze?

Is the talk of tawa wiser
Than the rata or the gum?
Is the sparkle of the totara
More profound than either one?

Or are you just returning
Your substance to the sun,
And I just use its burning
On your smoking journey home?

O my servant, my companion,
Cook my food and warm my bed.
Dry my clothes and keep me cosy,
Keep me safe and keep me fed.

And yet I have heard fierce wars being fought
In the hunger of your conflagration
And seen Tyrannosaurus Rex wink at me
From the embers of your glowing grave.

I'm still none the wiser and I suppose I'll go on
mucking around with fire right up until I wind up in the big
one.